The Open Univer

T357
Structural integrity:
designing against failure

BLOCK 1
STRESS ANALYSIS

PART 6: BENDING, TORSION AND BUCKLING
PART 7: RESIDUAL STRESS

This publication forms part of an Open University course T357 *Structural integrity: designing against failure*. Details of this and other Open University courses can be obtained from the Student Registration and Enquiry Service, The Open University, PO Box 197, Milton Keynes MK7 6BJ, United Kingdom: tel. +44 (0)845 300 60 90, email general-enquiries@open.ac.uk

Alternatively, you may visit the Open University website at http://www.open.ac.uk where you can learn more about the wide range of courses and packs offered at all levels by The Open University.

To purchase a selection of Open University course materials visit http://www.ouw.co.uk, or contact Open University Worldwide, Walton Hall, Milton Keynes MK7 6AA, United Kingdom for a brochure. tel. +44 (0)1908 858793; fax +44(0)1908 858787; email ouw-customer-services@open.ac.uk

The Open University
Walton Hall, Milton Keynes
MK7 6AA

First published 2007. Combined edition 2009.

Edited and designed by The Open University.

Typeset by SR Nova Pvt. Ltd, Bangalore, India.

Printed in the United Kingdom by Page Bros, Norwich.

ISBN 978 0 7492 5264 9

1.1

CONTENTS

CONTENTS

1 INTRODUCTION

So far in the course we have looked mainly at the effects of loads in terms of generating stresses, and assessed the stresses as normal and shear stresses. You have seen how loads are transmitted through structures, and how excessive stress can lead to the failure of a component.

I mentioned bending and torsion earlier in the course as examples of how loads can cause the distortion of a structure. In this part, we're going to cover these concepts more thoroughly. Bending, in particular, is an extremely important aspect of structural analysis, because it is much easier to generate a stress large enough to cause failure of a component by bending it than it is by applying a tensile or torsional force. For example, it's relatively easy to snap a pencil by bending it with your fingers, but virtually impossible to do so by pulling or twisting.

This part will give you the tools and understanding to deal with bending and torsion in design problems, as well as an understanding of the phenomenon of buckling.

First, let's take a step back and think about how things are designed to carry loads without failing. The shape and form of a structural member depends on the primary forces that it is intended to support (see Figure 6.1). So, a cable or a simple bar with either a square or a round cross section could be ideal for an axially loaded member in a pin-jointed structure, as long as the load always stays in tension.

The main selection criterion for a tie is either the tensile or yield strength of the material; the cross-sectional area of the tie is then selected based on the maximum load that the tie could be subjected to during service, plus an appropriate safety factor. If the extension (or the strain) of the member is a factor in the design, then the cross-sectional area can be modified accordingly to reduce the stress.

A *tie* is a member that is designed to carry tensile forces only.

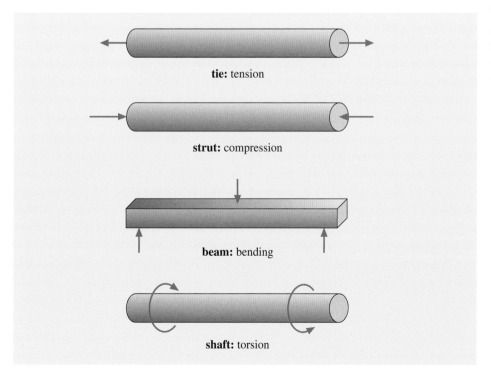

tie: tension

strut: compression

beam: bending

shaft: torsion

Figure 6.1 Basic one-dimensional structural members are categorized according to the primary forces they support

Figure 6.2 A buckled column

A structural member that is designed to carry predominantly compressive forces is called a *strut* or *column*.

Considering strength alone (or, more accurately, *compressive strength*), however, is not sufficient when designing structural members that are subject to axial compressive forces. For moderate forces, the member gets a little shorter because it is not perfectly rigid: it experiences a negative strain. But as the compressive load is increased, a critical value is reached at which the member, instead of shortening, buckles and usually breaks. *Buckling* is the most common stability failure in structures (Figure 6.2). A thin member in compression may support only a very small fraction of its compressive yield strength capability. Therefore, the profile (i.e. the cross-sectional shape), as well as the cross-sectional area, requires careful attention when designing a member that will be loaded in compression.

The use of a structure whose members are subject only to simple axial loads may appeal to engineers because it is relatively easy to analyse, but in practice this type of structure may not be the optimal choice for most designs. So, a set of stepping stones may be good for crossing a small stream, but something more practical is needed to span a valley (Figure 6.3). A simple *beam* across a short distance, for example, forms a suitable and cost-effective bridge for most purposes (Figure 6.4). The truss bridges we looked at in Part 5 reduce the bending in the structure and keep the forces in the members axial, although a truss bridge is not always the best solution in terms of cost, material or practicality.

Figure 6.3 (a) Stepping stones across a stream; (b) the Millau Viaduct, France, which needs a different design approach!

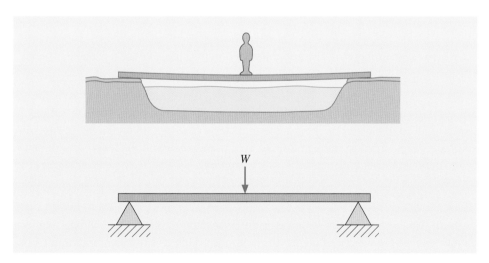

Figure 6.4 A beam across a stream is the simplest form of structure to do the job; note that I use the letter W to denote a weight load acting at a point

Beams are probably the most common form of structural element, and thus *bending* is the most common form of loading. The structural design of railways for monorail trains, which have become an alternative to underground trains in those urban areas where digging tunnels may no longer be possible, is a perfect example of the use of a beam as the main load-bearing member in a large structure (Figure 6.5a).

In Figure 6.5(b), I have introduced a new way of showing forces acting on a structure. A train or a bridge clearly does not have its load concentrated at a single point, so I have used an array of linked arrows to indicate that the load is spread across the length of the rail beneath the train.

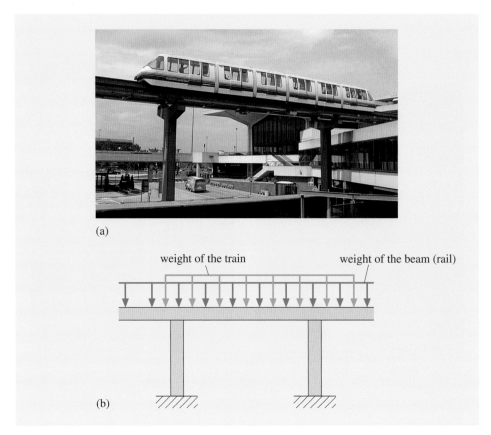

(a)

weight of the train   weight of the beam (rail)

(b)

Figure 6.5   (a) Beam structure of a monorail bridge; (b) the distribution of load on the beam between the supports. (The linked row of arrows represents the fact that the load is distributed over the whole of that length, rather than being concentrated at a point)

The assessment of a beam's strength is, however, far from simple. The internal forces induced in a beam by the loading transverse to its length are *bending moments* and *shear forces* (that is, moments about axes perpendicular to its length and forces acting perpendicular to its length); the resulting stress state in the member is more complicated than that produced by an axial loading.

The first requirement of a beam is that it can carry its own weight. The self-weight of the beam structure in Figure 6.5 is probably producing as much of a bending moment on the beam as the weight of the train, if not more. This is why beam bridges are not usually used for spanning long distances, unless intermediate supports (piers) are used, as in Figure 6.5. Even so, the relative simplicity and lower cost of beam bridges attract engineers to employ clever designs in order to make them viable alternatives to truss bridges even at longer span lengths. The roadway of the bridge shown in Figure 6.6 is constructed on a prestressed concrete beam supported by reinforced concrete piers that are 250 m apart. Look carefully at the figure and you will notice that the cross section of the beam is not constant: it gets thicker towards the piers, and the smallest cross section is mid-span. This is because the bending moment usually increases towards the supports, and the magnitude of the bending stresses can be reduced by increasing the depth, or thickness, of the beam section. I will cover this in more detail later in this part.

(a)

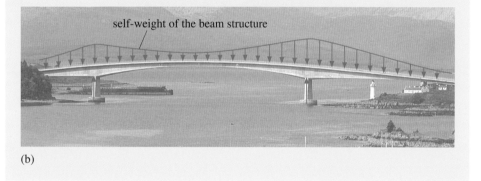

self-weight of the beam structure

(b)

Figure 6.6 (a) Skye Bridge, Scotland; (b) self-weight of the bridge shown as a distributed load

EXERCISE 6.1

Suggest why the design of the beam bridge shown in Figure 6.6 has an arched roadway, rather than a flat one. Surely this is not an environmentally friendly design, as the vehicles using this bridge will burn more fuel!

Even more ingenuity is required from the engineers who design aeroplane wings, which are prime examples of structures subject to bending. The demands on an aircraft-wing structure are severe (Figure 6.7). It is the wings that carry the weight of the aeroplane during flight and, of course, they must do so without deforming excessively by bending upwards; yet, when the plane is on the ground, the wings sag downwards under their own weight. The wing shape is decided by the designers of the aeroplane aerodynamics; the structural engineers then have the additional challenge of designing the wings at a minimum weight and cost, with absolute safety for the passengers when the aeroplane is in operation. Obviously, understanding the bending behaviour of structures is a prerequisite for this task.

Figure 6.7   Forces on an aircraft wing

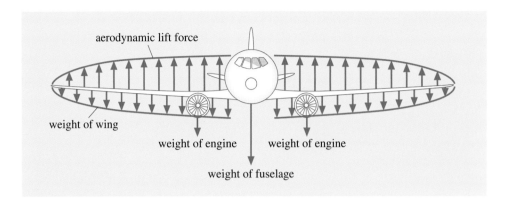

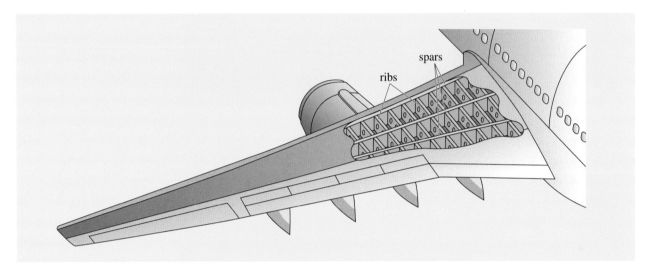

Figure 6.8   A schematic cut-away showing the internal structure of a modern passenger-aircraft wing

The wing of a modern aircraft is composed of a metal framework onto which the skin is riveted. Under the skin, the backbone of the wing structure is a pair, or sometimes more, of beams called spars, which carry the main bending loads (Figure 6.8).

In fact, the wing is not subject to bending loads only. There is a significant level of *torsional* loading in the wing structure, owing to the asymmetrical nature of the aerodynamic forces acting on the wing. *Torsion* is the engineering term used to describe a twisting moment, or torque, applied around the longitudinal axis of a structural member

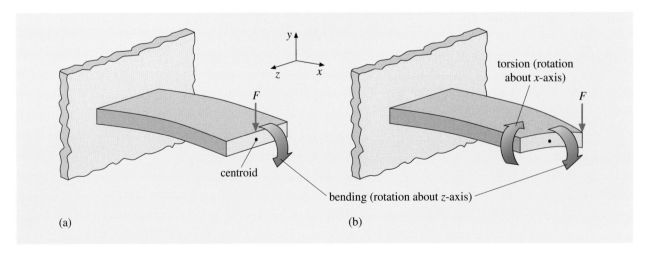

Figure 6.9   Cantilever (a) with a centrally applied load and (b) with off-axis loading

to produce rotational deformation (I showed this in Figure 6.1). The loading of the wing is analogous to the off-centre loading of a *cantilever*. When the load is centrally applied there is only bending deformation, but any deviation of the loading point from the centroid of the beam would cause the beam to twist about its longitudinal axis (Figure 6.9).

A beam fixed at only one end is called a cantilever.

Screwdrivers and drill bits are familiar objects subjected to torsional loadings (Figure 6.10a). The longest torsion members that I know of are the very long tubes used for drilling for oil, up to 10 km long (Figure 6.10b). Some of the most common examples of torsional loading are found in mechanical power transmission, such as typical motor-car drive shafts, shafts connecting turbines to the generators in hydroelectric power plants (Figure 6.10c), or the concentric shafts used in gas turbine engines (Figure 6.10d). You may recall from earlier in this block that the torsion of members with a circular cross section causes a stress state of pure shear in the member.

(a)

(b)

(c)

(d)

Figure 6.10 Torsion examples: (a) a drill; (b) an oil-rig drill; (c) the shaft that connects the turbine to the generator in a hydroelectric power plant; (d) a schematic cut-away of a modern gas turbine aero-engine, where the power transmission between the turbines, the compressors and the fan is achieved by means of concentric shafts that work under torsional loading

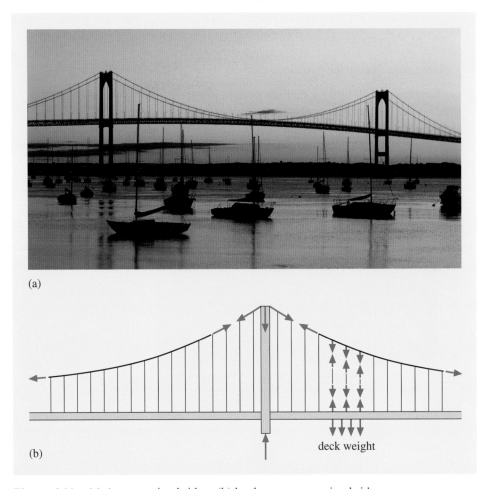

Figure 6.11   (a) A suspension bridge; (b) loads on a suspension bridge

Most structures do indeed consist of members subject to various forms of loading. For example, take a look at the suspension bridge in Figure 6.11. The roadway or deck hangs from the vertical cables, which must be in tension. The main suspension cables are anchored at their ends and pull down on the towers, putting the towers into compression. The deck, supported by the vertical cables and carrying the various traffic loads, is subject to bending, although it can be subjected to torsion as well due to asymmetric traffic loads and wind forces on the cables. A suspension-bridge structure, therefore, contains members that experience all four types of load.

The structural members I have considered so far (again, look back to Figure 6.1) are essentially 'one-dimensional', i.e. their lengths are large compared with their cross-sectional dimensions. They are assumed to transfer the loads in one direction only. Ties and struts transfer axial forces only; beams carry lateral forces by resisting bending; and shafts transfer torques.

What about two-dimensional members, the so-called 'surface elements' such as shells and membranes that were introduced in Part 5? Can I extend to two-dimensional elements the techniques I developed to assess the strength of one-dimensional members? The deck of a bridge, for example, is not really a beam, but more likely to behave like a *plate*, as its width is much larger than its depth. A plate is a two-dimensional structural member, loaded normal to its plane, so that, like a

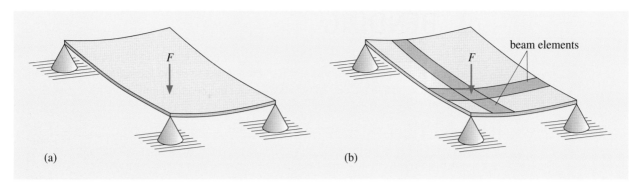

(a)   (b)

Figure 6.12   Bending of a plate due to a concentrated force

beam, it carries the load by bending (Figure 6.12a). Although the two-dimensional nature of the problem makes it much more complicated than a beam, as a first approximation it is often acceptable to visualize the loaded plate by breaking it down into two separate beam elements, as shown in Figure 6.12(b). Many structures, such as aircraft skins, bridge decks, floors and laptop-computer casings, can be idealized as plates, but their configurations are often more complex than that shown in Figure 6.12(b). Therefore, the analysis of these two-dimensional problems is usually performed using numerical modelling such as finite element analysis.

In the rest of this part, therefore, I will concentrate on the analysis of one-dimensional structural members subject to bending and torsion, before finishing with a look at the phenomenon of buckling.

2   BENDING

The bending analysis of beams is probably the most widely used stress-analysis method in engineering. In this section, I am going to begin the study of bending with the simplest possible case: a length of beam bent by equal and opposite ☑ **couples** ☑ acting in the same longitudinal plane (Figure 6.13).

☑ Couples

A pair of forces that are equal in magnitude but opposite in direction and that act on parallel lines (like those at points A and B, and C and D, in the beam shown in Figure 6.13) is called a *couple*. There is no net force, but because they do not act along the same line they do have a resultant moment.

When representing forces on a diagram, a couple such as that involving the forces at C and D can be represented, as shown in Figure 6.13(b), as a turning moment instead.

The loading shown in Figure 6.13(b) is known as *pure bending*, as there is no other force present in the beam. By analysing this simple loading case, the results obtained can be applied to other, more complex, situations where bending occurs, as you will see.

2.1   Bending stresses

A complexity of bending is that, unlike axial stresses in structural members with uniform cross-sectional areas, bending stresses are not distributed evenly through the cross section of a beam. Whereas an axially loaded member will either extend or shorten, a beam subjected to pure bending by opposite and equal couples will curve (or *flex*), as shown in Figure 6.14(a), which results in the extension of one side of the beam and the shortening of the opposite side. This means that the stresses and strains will not be constant over the beam's cross section.

Figure 6.13   Pure bending of a beam by a pair of opposite but equal couples

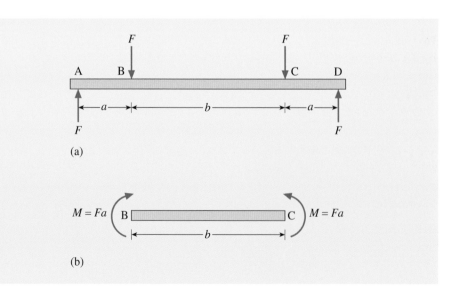

Since I am looking at elastic bending, and the force in the beam from the bending is uniaxial, I can obtain a relation for bending stress simply as:

$$\sigma_x = \varepsilon_x E = \frac{Ey}{R} \tag{6.2}$$

which describes the linear stress distribution shown in Figure 6.14(b). Equations (6.1) and (6.2) are useful because they allow us to determine stress and strain in a beam if we know its radius of curvature. This is illustrated in the following example.

EXAMPLE

A manufacturer of electrical-grade copper wire distributes its products wound in reels, as shown in Figure 6.20. For a new product, 0.2 mm diameter copper wire, the manufacturer wants to choose a reel diameter such that, when the wire is wound around the reel, the maximum bending stress generated in the wire does not exceed the yield strength of the wire. What should be the minimum radius r for the reel if the yield strength and the elastic modulus of copper are 60 MPa and 124 GPa respectively?

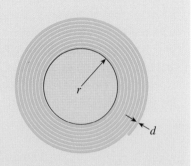

Figure 6.20   A reel of copper wire

SOLUTION

The longitudinal stress due to bending is inversely proportional to the radius of curvature through Equation (6.2). The maximum stress occurs when the radius of curvature is the smallest, i.e. at the first winding of the wire on the reel.

Rearranging Equation (6.2) gives:

$$R = \frac{Ey}{\sigma_x}$$

The maximum stress in the wire occurs at the outer edges of the wire, when $y = \pm\, d/2$. The minimum radius that the wire can sustain without the outer edges of the wire exceeding the yield strength of copper is then obtained by substituting the yield stress for σ_x:

$$R = \frac{E(d/2)}{\sigma_x}$$

$$= \frac{124 \times 10^9 \ \text{Pa} \times 0.1 \times 10^{-3} \ \text{m}}{60 \times 10^6 \ \text{Pa}}$$

$$= 0.207 \ \text{m}$$

Therefore the minimum radius chosen for the reel should be 0.207 m.

Note that the radius of curvature should really be measured from the neutral axis of the wire's cross section, so that I should really add on half the wire's diameter to get the 'right' answer. However, since the radius of the wire is much smaller than R, the inclusion of wire radius in the equation will not make any significant difference in this case.

EXERCISE 6.2

The reel of wire shown in Figure 6.21 has a central core of diameter 20 mm, wrapped with a solder wire of diameter 1 mm. The wire has a yield stress of 40 MPa and an elastic modulus of 50 GPa. Calculate whether the yield stress is exceeded when the wire is wound onto the reel.

Figure 6.21   A reel of solder wire

We are almost halfway through the development of bending theory. The next step is to find the relation between the stress in the beam and the bending moment acting on the beam; see ▽ **Stress, bending moments and moments of area** ▽.

▽ Stress, bending moments and moments of area

The beam shown in Figure 6.22 is subjected to pure bending, so that the top surface of the beam is in tension. Consider a small strip of material with an area of dA on the cross section of the beam at a distance $+y$ from the neutral axis. The tensile stress acting on the strip, σ_x, produces a force in the strip equal to the stress times the area of the strip, i.e. $\sigma_x\, dA$. This force produces a moment about the neutral axis equal to the force multiplied by the distance, i.e. $\sigma_x\, dA \times y$. The total moment M produced over the entire cross section is found by adding up *all* such moments over the whole area. Mathematically, this is equivalent

to integrating with respect to the whole cross-sectional area A:

$$M = \int_A y\sigma_x\, dA$$

Substituting into this equation the expression for σ_x that I derived in Equation (6.2) gives:

$$M = \int_A y\left(\frac{Ey}{R}\right)dA$$

In this expression, the elastic modulus of the material E and the radius of curvature R are constant. So, they can be taken out of the integration process to give:

$$M = \frac{E}{R} \int_A y^2 \, \mathrm{d}A \qquad (6.3)$$

Now, the integral term left in the equation, $\int_A y^2 \, \mathrm{d}A$, is purely a geometrical expression. It provides a measure of the effectiveness of the particular geometry of beam to resist bending. It is a property of the section of the beam and is known as its *second moment of area*, denoted by the letter I.

Moments of area

The *second moment of area* is an essential part of bending analysis. (You may come across this elsewhere referred to as the *moment of inertia of area*). It provides a measure of the effectiveness of a particular beam's cross-sectional shape and area to resist bending deformation: the larger the second moment of area is, the better the resistance to bending will be.

The second moment of area is calculated for any cross-sectional shape using:

$$I = \int_A y^2 \, \mathrm{d}A \qquad (6.4)$$

I will take you through an example of how this equation is used to calculate the second moment of area of a beam. You will never be asked to do this; it's something that, if you need to know, you'll be given or you'll find from a standard set of tables. It is useful to understand how it is obtained, though, so that you can see the physical foundation for its use.

As an example, consider the beam with a rectangular cross-sectional area shown in Figure 6.22. I have put the origin of the reference axes at the centroid of the section, which is also the geometric centre of the rectangle. As the plane of bending is confined to the xy-plane, the bending deformation would occur about the z-axis, which is the neutral axis for this particular case of loading. Therefore, I need to find the second moment of area of the beam about the z-axis, denoted I_z.

Now, in order to employ Equation (6.4) for this purpose, consider an element on the cross section in the form of a thin strip of width b and height $\mathrm{d}y$, as shown in Figure 6.23. The second moment of this single element about the z-axis is given by using Equation (6.4), where $\mathrm{d}A$ is the area of the element, i.e. $\mathrm{d}A = b \, \mathrm{d}y$. The second moment of area of the beam is found by adding all such elements on the entire cross section. Mathematically, this is equivalent to integrating $y^2 \, \mathrm{d}A$ between the limits of the top of the rectangle ($+h/2$) and the bottom ($-h/2$), so that:

$$
\begin{aligned}
I_z &= \int_{-h/2}^{+h/2} y^2 \, \mathrm{d}A \\
&= \int_{-h/2}^{+h/2} y^2 b \, \mathrm{d}y = \left[\frac{by^3}{3} \right]_{-h/2}^{+h/2} \\
&= \frac{b(h/2)^3}{3} - \frac{b(-h/2)^3}{3} \\
&= \frac{bh^3}{12} \qquad (6.5)
\end{aligned}
$$

I_z, therefore, has SI units of m^4.

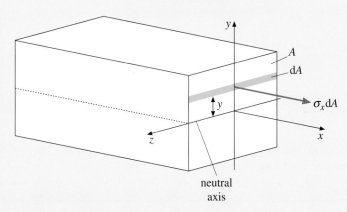

Figure 6.22   Section of a beam that is subjected to pure bending

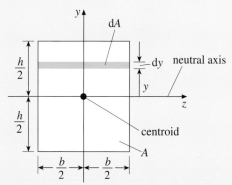

Figure 6.23   Cross section of a beam subjected to pure bending about the z-axis

EXAMPLE

Can you explain, in light of the above result, why bending a ruler across its width, as in Figure 6.24(a), is more difficult than bending it across its thickness, as in Figure 6.24(b)?

SOLUTION

Equation (6.5) tells us that the bending stiffness of a beam with a rectangular section is mostly determined by its height h, as I depends on h^3. The height of the ruler when it is bent as in Figure 6.24(a) is much larger than when it is bent as in Figure 6.24(b), so it has a much larger value of second moment of area. The ruler, of course, has the same cross-sectional area in both orientations shown in Figure 6.24, but the area is distributed differently in each case; much more of the area lies away from the neutral axis for the former case and hence there is greater resistance to rotation about the neutral axis.

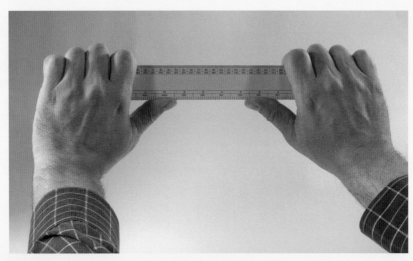

(a)

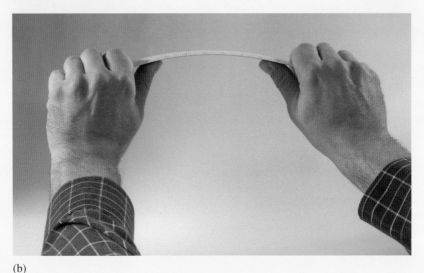

(b)

Figure 6.24   Bending a ruler is more difficult across (a) its width than (b) its thickness

EXERCISE 6.3

It is possible to quantify the difference in bending resistances by comparing the second moment of area for the two cases. My plastic ruler has cross-sectional dimensions of approximately 3.5 mm by 38 mm. Assuming it is a perfect rectangular section (which isn't quite right, but will do as an approximation), the second moment of area for the ruler may be calculated using Equation (6.5).

Calculate I for bending in the two different orientations shown in Figure 6.24.   △

The second moments of area of most common shapes used in beam design can be obtained from a table of standard solutions: Table 6.1 provides some examples. The second moments of area of built-up sections, i.e. a hollow rectangle, a hollow circle and an I-section (or I-beam), can be simply obtained by subtracting the I of the missing parts from the I of the overall outline of the shape, providing that the sections are symmetrical about the neutral axes. (Note that the sections are subject to loading in a vertical plane, i.e. a plane of bending, at right angles to the neutral axis nn' passing through the centre of the area.)

EXERCISE 6.4

Write a formula for the second moment of area of the section shown in Figure 6.25 using the information provided in Table 6.1.   △

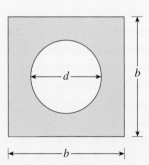

Figure 6.25 Cross section of a beam for Exercise 6.4

Now, we have seen that I is called the second moment of area. Is there a *first* moment of area? Yes, it is $\int y \, dA$, and it is used to define the centroid of an area, and hence the position of the neutral axis in bending analysis. The centroid of an area in, say, the yz-plane shown in Figure 6.23 is defined by the

Table 6.1   Second moments of area for some common cross sections

Section	Second moment of area about the neutral axis nn'
solid rectangle 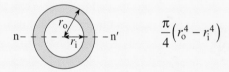	$\dfrac{bh^3}{12}$
hollow rectangle 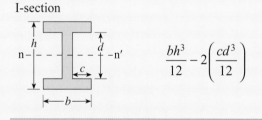	$\dfrac{bh^3}{12} - \dfrac{b_i h_i^3}{12}$
solid circle	$\dfrac{\pi r^4}{4}$
hollow circle	$\dfrac{\pi}{4}\left(r_o^4 - r_i^4\right)$
I-section	$\dfrac{bh^3}{12} - 2\left(\dfrac{cd^3}{12}\right)$

condition that the first moments of area about the centroidal axes are both zero, so that $\int_A y \, dA = 0$ and $\int_A z \, dA = 0$. However, I am not going to ask you to use these equations to find the centroids and neutral axes of sections in this course, as the sections we will study will be mostly symmetrical shapes, as in Table 6.1, and when necessary such information will be provided for you.   △

SAQ 6.1 (Learning outcomes 6.2 and 6.3)

A cross section such as that shown in Figure 6.25 might be used in order to reduce the weight of a beam, by removing material from around the neutral axis. For a beam with $b = 50$ mm, calculate the value of I:

(a) with no hole in the beam cross section

(b) with a hole of diameter 30 mm removed from the beam centre as in Figure 6.25.

SAQ 6.1 shows that the contribution of the material away from the beam centre is what really contributes to the bending resistance of a beam. In this particular case, removing nearly 30% of the material in the beam produced a change of less than 10% in its bending resistance.

Equation (6.3) can be rewritten as:

$$M = \frac{EI}{R} \tag{6.6}$$

By combining Equations (6.2) and (6.6) we can put all the key parameters in bending into one expression:

$$\frac{M}{I} = \frac{\sigma}{y} = \frac{E}{R} \tag{6.7}$$

This equation is known as the *engineer's theory of bending* (or the *engineer's bending equation*). It is one of the key tools of the trade in stress analysis. Knowing the applied forces, we can make a calculation of the bending moment M; you will gain some practice in this in the coming sections. Then, knowing the beam geometry, I can be obtained, usually by consulting a table of standard values. From this, we can determine the stresses in the beam, or more usually just the stress at the surface, which is of most interest because this is where the peak stresses occur in bending.

You just pick the appropriate parts of the equation to solve a given problem; you don't need to work with all six unknowns. See the following example for an illustration.

EXAMPLE

A beam with a section as given in Figure 6.25 is made of a material that can sustain a maximum stress of 200 MPa in tension and compression. If the dimensions of the section are $b = 40$ mm and $d = 25$ mm, calculate the maximum bending moment that can be applied to the beam.

SOLUTION

The maximum bending moment can be calculated from the engineer's bending equation:

$$\frac{M}{I} = \frac{\sigma}{y}$$

by rearranging it as:

$$M = \frac{\sigma I}{y}$$

The second moment of area of the section is calculated by the formula obtained in Exercise 6.4 as:

$$
\begin{aligned}
I &= \frac{b^4}{12} - \frac{\pi r^4}{4} \\
&= \frac{\left(40 \times 10^{-3}\ \text{m}\right)^4}{12} - \frac{\pi \left(12.5 \times 10^{-3}\ \text{m}\right)^4}{4} \\
&= 1.94 \times 10^{-7}\ \text{m}^4
\end{aligned}
$$

The maximum stress at the section occurs at the farthest distance from the neutral axis, which is when $y = b/2 = 20$ mm. Substituting into the rearranged bending equation gives:

$$M_{\text{max}} = \frac{200 \times 10^6\ \text{N m}^{-2} \times 1.94 \times 10^{-7}\ \text{m}^4}{20 \times 10^{-3}\ \text{m}} = 1.94 \times 10^3\ \text{N m} = 1.94\ \text{kN m}$$

EXERCISE 6.5

A beam with a cross section as shown in Figure 6.25 is made from an aluminium alloy with a Young's modulus of 70 GPa. If the dimensions of the section are $b = 50$ mm and $d = 35$ mm, calculate the maximum stress at the surface of the beam when it is subjected to a pure bending moment of magnitude 2 kN m about its z-axis.

Writing the engineer's bending equation as:

$$\sigma = \frac{My}{I}$$

is useful in relating the longitudinal stress to the bending moment and the geometry of the beam.

This equation shows that the longitudinal stress in a beam varies linearly with distance y from the neutral axis. So, the maximum stress in the section occurs at the farthest points from the neutral axis, i.e. at the outer edges of the beam's section where $y = y_{\text{max}}$. The design, or selection, of beams for a particular job (i.e. for a given bending moment) usually requires that the maximum stress in the section does not exceed an allowable stress. It is obvious from the above equation that, in order to use the material to maximum advantage, the designer would aim to increase the value of I while keeping beam height (y_{max}) as small as possible, for a given cross-sectional area. The ratio I/y_{max} is therefore an indication of how efficiently the material is being used. This ratio is frequently used in design calculations for beam sections and it is called the *section modulus*, denoted by the letter Z.

Figure 6.26   Steel I-beam sections are widely used in the construction industry

For efficient use of material, beams should be designed with as large a section modulus as possible. The primary example of such a design is the *I-beam* (or I-section), which has a large proportion of its cross-sectional area located far from the section's neutral axis, and consequently has a large value of *I* and hence *Z*. Steel I-beams are very widely used in the construction of bridges and buildings (Figure 6.26) and therefore are available in a variety of standard sizes.

SAQ 6.2 (Learning outcomes 6.1, 6.2 and 6.3)

A mild steel I-beam, whose section is shown in Figure 6.27, is subjected to a pure bending moment of magnitude 200 kN m about its *z*-axis. The Young's modulus of the steel is 210 GPa. Calculate the maximum bending stress in:

(a) the web

(b) the flange.

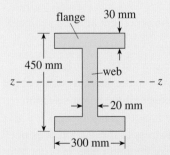

Figure 6.27   I-beam section for SAQ 6.2. The 'web' is the central connecting part of the beam and the 'flange' is the section that is loaded

2.2 Stress concentrations in bending

Not all structural members subjected to bending have a uniform cross section along their length. Examples include shoulder fillets and grooves in shafts, rivet or bolt holes in beams, and gear teeth (Figure 6.28).

When there is a sudden change in the cross section of the beam, the distribution of the bending stresses will have to be adjusted to take into account the stress-concentration effect. This is achieved by the use of a stress concentration factor K_b for bending, rather similar to K_t, which we used to modify the tensile stress at notches back in Part 3. In this case, the magnitude of the bending stress is scaled with the stress concentration factor for bending. Modifying the bending stress relation in Equation (6.7) gives:

$$\sigma = K_b \frac{My}{I} \qquad\qquad (6.8)$$

Figure 6.29 shows the variation of the stress concentration factor under pure bending for two geometries: beams with rectangular cross sections containing fillets or grooves.

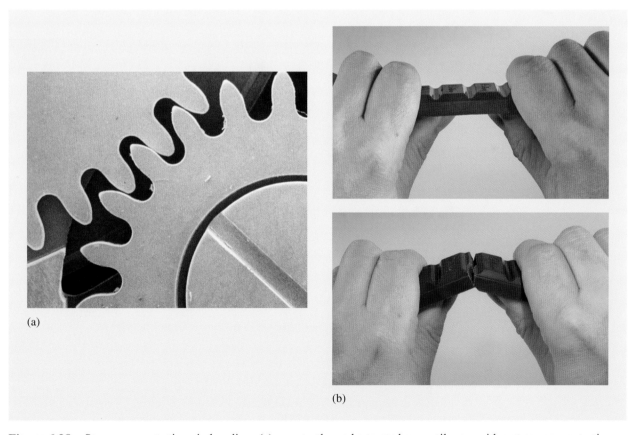

(a)

(b)

Figure 6.28   Stress concentrations in bending: (a) gear teeth can be treated as cantilevers with a stress concentration at their root; (b) without the stress-concentration effect of grooves, sharing thick chocolate bars equally wouldn't be so easy

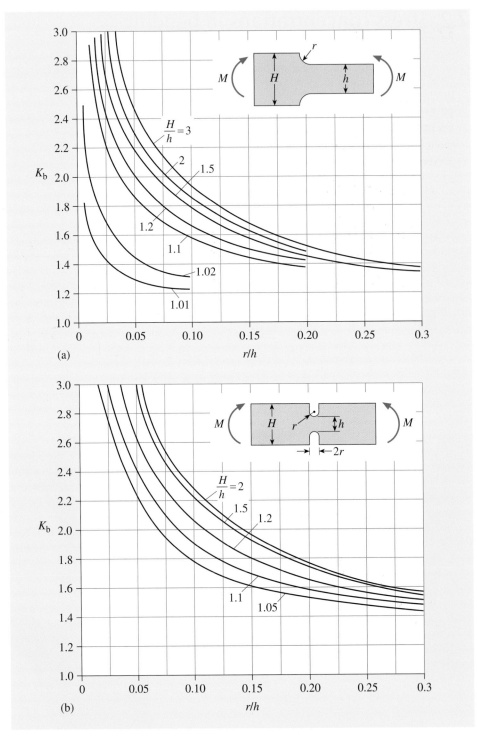

Figure 6.29   Stress concentration factors for rectangular sections with (a) fillets and (b) grooves under pure bending; adapted from Pilkey, W.D. (1997), Peterson's Stress Concentration Factors (2nd edn), Wiley & Sons, Inc, p. 159 and p. 105

EXERCISE 6.6

The stress in the root of a gear tooth loaded at its tip may be estimated, as an initial approach, by assuming it behaves as a flat bar with fillets subjected to pure bending, as shown in Figure 6.30. Calculate the maximum stress in the gear tooth if the applied bending moment is 100 N m. The dimensions of the gear tooth are $H = 50$ mm, $h = 20$ mm, $b = 12$ mm and $r = 5$ mm. The elastic modulus of the gear material is 210 GPa. You will need to use the information on stress concentration factors provided in Figure 6.29.

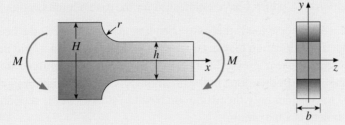

Figure 6.30   Flat bar with fillets as a gear tooth

SAQ 6.3 (Learning outcomes 6.1, 6.3 and 6.4)

During a house restoration project, an electrician cut symmetrical grooves into the top and bottom of some load-bearing beams to run electrical cables along (Figure 6.31). The height H and width b of the beams are 100 mm and 40 mm respectively. The minimum necessary depth of each groove is $2r = 10$ mm, but for aesthetic reasons the electrician decided to increase the groove depth to $2r = 25$ mm. Calculate the increase in stress for each of the groove depths of 10 mm and 25 mm if the applied bending moment is 300 N m.

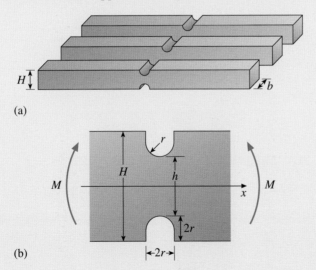

(a)

(b)

Figure 6.31   (a) Beams with symmetrical grooves; (b) geometry of the grooves

2.3 Internal forces in beams

So far, I have assumed that the beams I have analysed were subject to pure bending. In general, though, the bending of beams is not produced by pure bending moments, but by point loads or distributed loads acting perpendicular (or transverse) to the length of the beam. Consequently, the bending moment varies along the beam; so, in order to decide whether a beam is strong enough for a given loading, I need to find out where in the beam the magnitude of the bending moment is the greatest. Once I have determined the maximum bending moment (or the value of it at a particular section that I am interested in), the bending stresses can be found by the use of the *engineer's bending equation* (Equation 6.7), which I have established for the case of pure bending.

Furthermore, the transverse loads that cause bending also act to shear the beam, so there is the added complication that shear stresses will be present in a bent beam. Generally, though, the shear stresses in a beam are an order of magnitude smaller than the bending stresses; therefore, at the preliminary stages of beam design, engineers need to consider only the maximum bending stresses at the section where the bending moment is a maximum.

In this section, I will show you how the internal forces are determined from the applied transverse loads. But first, I want to clarify a few points about external loading and the beam supports.

2.3.1 Supports and loads on beams

Beams are normally analysed separately from the rest of a structure as isolated bodies, but the way the beam is joined to the structure has to be modelled correctly, as this determines how the beam carries the load. Look at the simple structure shown in Figure 6.32(a), a beam across a stream, with a load applied vertically in the middle.

Figure 6.32   (a) Beam across a stream, (b) simplified sketch and (c) its free-body diagram

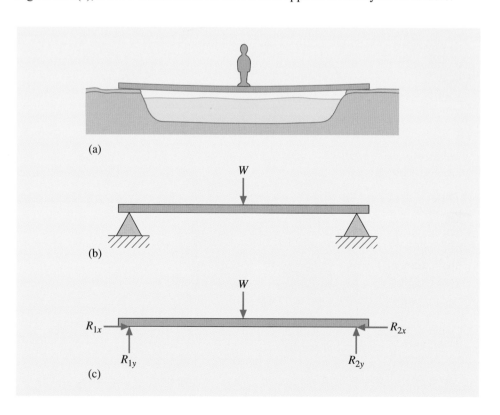

The applied load is transferred to the ground through the load-bearing contact points at the ends. The ends are free to rotate (just like a pinned joint) and so do not carry any bending moment. The beam can, therefore, be modelled as resting on knife-edges that allow rotation, but not sideways or downward movement (Figure 6.32b). Figure 6.32(c) shows the free-body diagram of the beam, including the support reactions.

It may appear that I don't have enough information to calculate the forces acting on the beam, but by using the symmetry of the beam and the loading, and some common sense, I can simplify the problem when ▽ **calculating the support reactions** ▽.

Figure 6.33 shows the main methods of supporting beams, and the associated support reaction forces. The first two are called *simple* supports, since the beam is assumed to simply rest upon knife-edges or rollers. Both the knife-edge and the roller allow rotations, just like pinned joints. The roller support is free to move sideways also, but it restrains the movement vertically. Therefore, there is only a vertical reaction at a roller support. The knife-edge additionally restricts horizontal movement; so there are two reactions, one horizontal and one vertical, at a knife-edge support. In general, the term *simply supported beam* in mechanics problems is used to describe beams resting on a roller support at one end and a knife-edge support at the other, because this forms a basic, statically determinate structure.

If the beam is fixed – that is, clamped or solidly cast into a wall or the ground, for example – it prevents all translations and rotations at the built-in support point.

The roller support is more appropriately known as a *knife-edge on rollers*, but I will call it a roller for short to avoid confusion with the *fixed knife-edge*.

▽ Calculating the support reactions

Is it possible to determine the unknown reaction forces in Figure 6.32(c)? As it stands, this structure is statically indeterminate, since there are four unknowns (R_{1x}, R_{1y}, R_{2x} and R_{2y}), one more than the available equilibrium equations (i.e. the equilibrium of forces in the horizontal direction $\sum F_x = 0$, the equilibrium of forces in the vertical direction $\sum F_y = 0$ and the equilibrium of moments $\sum M = 0$). However, the horizontal reaction forces will be zero, or at least negligibly small, for small deflections of the beam, as long as the applied load W is perpendicular to the beam; that is:

$$R_{1x} = R_{2x} = 0$$

This additional equation balances the number of available equations with the number of unknowns, which makes the structure statically determinate.

The additional equation required to make a structure statically determinate is known as the *equation of condition* and can often be obtained if there is some symmetry to the problem being studied. So, for example, a further equation of condition could be obtained for the beam in Figure 6.32 if the point of application of W is exactly in the centre of the beam. From symmetry, you would expect the vertical reactions to be equal in that case; so:

$$R_{1y} = R_{2y}$$

Thus, the unknown reaction forces can be found by considering the vertical equilibrium alone.

Figure 6.33 Basic beam-support types and associated reactions; a knife-edge is only a model of the support – in reality a pin or hinge is typically used

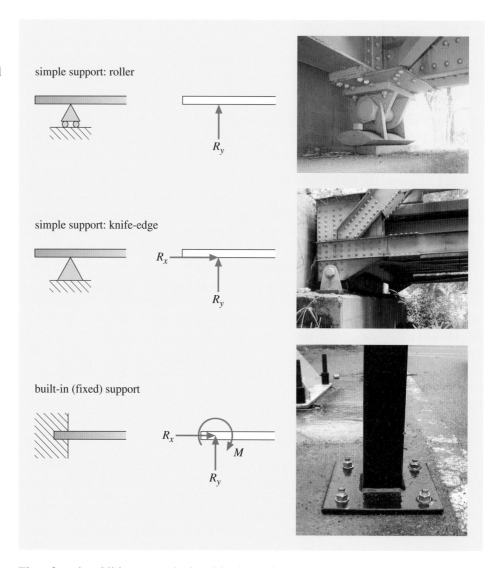

simple support: roller

simple support: knife-edge

built-in (fixed) support

Therefore, in addition to vertical and horizontal reactions (with respect to the beam axis), there is also a moment reaction at the built-in supports. A beam fixed at one end only is called a *cantilever*.

The choice of support type to analyse a particular problem may not be straightforward, and it is a matter of experience and judgement to model the supports accurately. For example, a roof girder may appear to be rigidly built into a wall, but there can be no guarantee that the masonry and mortar are absolutely firm and rigid, so perhaps a simple-support model would be more appropriate. If in doubt, you can always consider all the possible options and design for the worst case – whichever one generates the highest loads.

Now let us look at the types of load applied to the beams. External loads can be modelled as three basic types: point loads (also referred to as *concentrated* loads), distributed loads and external moments (Figure 6.34). Point loads are assumed to act on an infinitesimally small length of beam and are represented by single arrows. Of course, this is an idealisation, otherwise there would be an infinite stress at the point of contact. In practice, the load acts over a finite area: the weight of the person standing on the beam in Figure 6.32 is spread over an area equivalent to his or her footprints. However, the point load assumption is often a valid and useful approximation for analysis purposes.

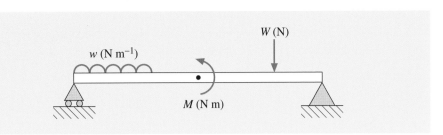

Figure 6.34   External loads on a simply supported beam

The distributed loads I shall consider in this course, as in real-life cases, will be *uniformly distributed loads* (UDLs) and will be quoted as load or force per unit length, otherwise called a *load intensity*, with the units of newtons per metre ($N\ m^{-1}$). This is a useful way of representing the self-weight of real structural beams that have uniform cross sections. UDLs are represented diagrammatically by 'piles of sand' or, on a free-body diagram, as a linked row of force arrows. External moments are indicated by a curved arrow.

When determining the reaction forces using the equilibrium equations, a uniformly distributed load may be replaced by an equivalent point load to simplify the calculations. The total load applied on the beam by the UDL is found by multiplying the load intensity w by the length l over which the UDL acts, and then placing the resulting force at the mid-position of the UDL. But note that the simplification of a UDL as a point load is done for the purposes of calculating the reaction forces *only*. It is not a valid simplification, for example, when the internal forces in the beam are calculated, as you will see in Section 2.3.4.

The first step in analysing a beam is to draw the free-body diagram and calculate the support reactions by considering equilibrium, just like you did in the analysis of pin-jointed structures in Part 5. As well as providing revision, the following exercise will show you how a UDL on a beam may be replaced by an equivalent point load when calculating the support reactions.

EXERCISE 6.7

Figure 6.35 shows a simply supported beam subjected to a uniformly distributed load and a point load.

(a) Draw the free-body diagram of the beam, indicating the reactions.

(b) Check whether the beam is statically determinate, assuming that the UDL and the point load are known.

(c) Calculate the support reactions if w is 5 kN m^{-1}, $W = 20$ kN, $l = 4$ m and $L = 10$ m.

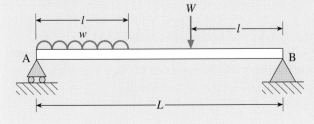

Figure 6.35 Analysis of a simply supported beam with a UDL and a point load

The answer to the last exercise provides a useful general simplification for the analysis of beam problems: for problems where all the applied loads are perpendicular to the beam, the horizontal reaction forces can be ignored.

The following exercise shows how to calculate the moment reaction at the built-in support of a cantilever.

EXERCISE 6.8

A wooden diving board is 3 m long, 0.4 m wide and 0.1 m thick (Figure 6.36a). The distributed load on the beam is its self-weight.

Figure 6.36(b) shows the free-body diagram of the cantilever, where there is a vertical reaction force and a moment reaction at the built-in end. Notice that I have omitted the horizontal reaction at the built-in support as it is zero, because all the forces are acting perpendicular to the beam.

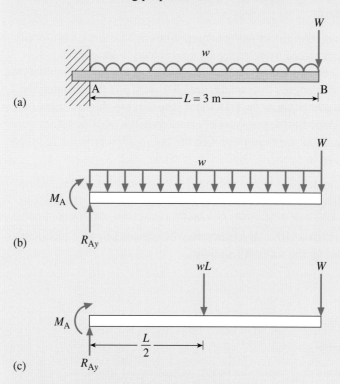

Figure 6.36   Cantilever for Exercise 6.8

(a) Is this structure statically determinate?

(b) Using the dimensions of the board, calculate the self-weight of the beam. Express the self-weight as a UDL (or load intensity). Take the density of the wood to be 400 kg m^{-3}.

(c) Figure 6.36(c) gives the free-body diagram, after substituting the UDL with a point load applied at the midpoint of the beam. Calculate the support reactions when a person weighing 700 N stands on the free end of the board, taking into account the self-weight of the board.

SAQ 6.4 (Learning outcomes 6.5 and 6.6)

Draw the free-body diagrams of the beams given in Figure 6.37, indicating the support reactions. Determine whether they are statically determinate and, if they are, calculate the reactions.

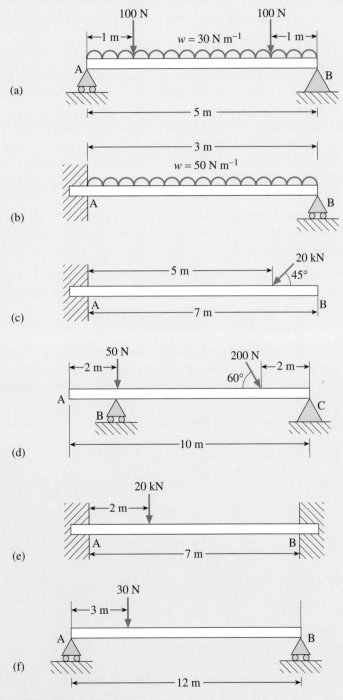

Figure 6.37   Beams for SAQ 6.4

2.3.2 Shear-force and bending-moment diagrams

We have already seen that external loads applied to a structural member are transmitted to the next member, or to the ground, by internal forces developed in the member.

Transverse loads applied to a beam cause three types of internal force: bending moments, shear forces and axial forces. Determination of the magnitude and variation of these forces within the beam is an essential part of the design process. Once these forces are determined, the stress state inside the beam can then be calculated.

How do we determine these internal forces? Once more, they are found by the most basic idea underlying all the theory of force and load systems that we have looked at so far in structural analysis, i.e. the principle of static equilibrium. What I will cover in this section, therefore, won't introduce any new principles, rather I will be applying what you already know to new problems. Also, I'll treat the answers slightly differently: up to now I've tended to work towards a point where I can find numerical answers to a problem. Here, as you'll see, I'll try to use the solution to plot a general diagram (a graph) of how the shear force and bending moments vary within differently loaded beams. You may find this pictorial approach more helpful in imagining what happens inside loaded beams. In any case, I will use lots of examples to expose how these methods work.

Consider the free-body diagram of a simply supported beam subjected to a point load F at an angle to the beam, as shown in Figure 6.38(a). Now, for the purpose of finding the internal forces, imagine the beam is cut vertically on plane CC′, splitting it into two free-body diagrams as shown in Figure 6.38(b).

The principle of equilibrium should apply to each portion of the beam, otherwise each portion would move under the influence of external forces. So, it is clear that additional forces need to act on the imaginary cut faces of the beam to balance the forces in each free-body diagram. I have added three forces at each cut face: a shear force F_s, an axial force F_n and a bending moment M. These forces can be thought

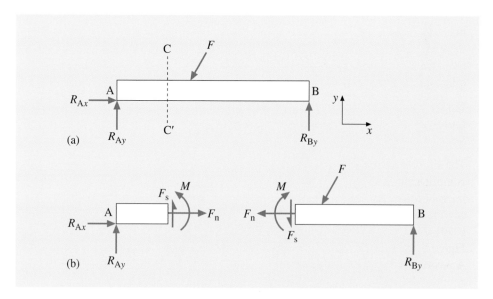

Figure 6.38   Internal forces on imaginary cut faces of a beam

of as imaginary external forces that would keep the cut beam in equilibrium by producing the same deformations as in the uncut beam. Notice that the forces on each cut face are equal in magnitude but opposite in direction, so when the two portions are put together there is no resultant force at that point.

Why do I need more than one force to keep the cut beams in equilibrium? If you remember from Part 5, the equilibrium of bodies that are subjected to *non-concurrent* forces requires at least a force and a moment reaction. Now, look at the left-hand portion of the cut beam. The vertical reaction, if left unopposed, would both move the cut beam upwards and rotate it clockwise about the cut face. Therefore, it requires an opposing force to balance the upward translation and a moment to prevent the rotation. In addition, horizontal equilibrium requires that there is an axial force at the cut surface to balance the horizontal support reaction.

Note that although it seems to require two forces and a moment to balance the cut beam, this is due to my preference for resolving the forces into their components in the xy reference frame for convenience. Otherwise I would need, in addition to M, only the *resultant* of the forces F_s and F_n at the cut face for the equilibrium of the beam.

The internal forces F_s, F_n and M are found in the usual way, by considering the equilibrium of forces and moments in the free-body diagram of the cut beam. As these forces would usually vary through the length of the beam, the above procedure, i.e. cutting and finding internal forces at the cut surface, may need to be repeated at critical loc ations in the beam to obtain the complete distribution. Performing the analysis at a single location may not be sufficient.

When applying this technique to determine the internal force distribution in beams, it is important to adopt a ☑ **sign convention for bending** ☑ that is consistent in all the problems.

Note that F_s on the left-hand side of the cut in Figure 6.37 isn't drawn so as to oppose the reaction force; the directions of these unknown forces are chosen by the sign convention I introduced in Part 5.

☑ Sign convention for bending

There is no standardized sign convention for bending, because there isn't an overriding advantage of one particular convention over the others. However, there are some common practices amongst structural and civil engineers. I will use such a system in this course, while being careful to be consistent with the other sign conventions I have introduced.

First, for external loads, i.e. applied forces and support reactions, the positive forces act in the positive x- and y-directions in a two-dimensional system. So, forces pointing upwards and to the right in an xy reference frame are positive.

The sign convention for internal forces at cut faces is slightly more complicated, as they appear in pairs in the complementary cut faces. The internal forces on both cut faces of Figure 6.38(b) are all positive. Here, I define a cut face as positive or negative: for horizontally laid beams, a cut facing the positive x-direction, like the cut face on the left-hand free-body diagram in Figure 6.38(b), is positive, and a cut facing the negative x-direction is negative. A positive face would have *positive* axial and shear forces acting in *positive* x- and y-directions. A negative face would have *positive* axial and shear forces acting in *negative* x- and y-directions. ▷

The sign convention for bending moments is such that a positive bending moment causes anticlockwise rotation at a positive cut face and clockwise rotation at a negative cut face, as in Figure 6.38(b).

Probably an easier way of remembering the sign convention for bending moment is that the positive bending moment causes *sagging* of the beam and the negative bending moment causes *hogging*, as shown in Figure 6.39.

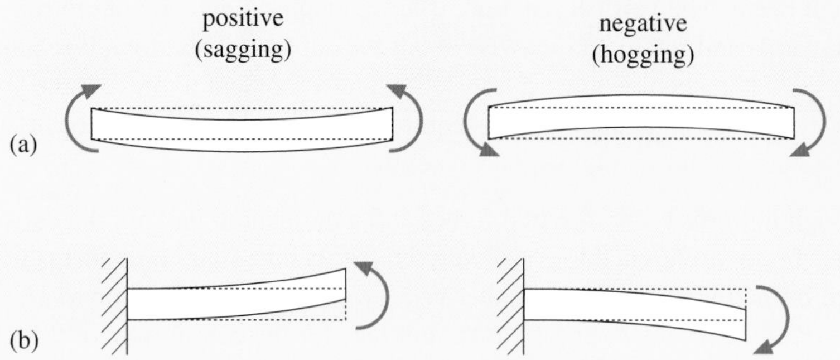

positive   negative
(sagging)   (hogging)

(a)

(b)

Figure 6.39   Sign convention for bending moments: (a) in a beam; (b) in a cantilever

2.3.3 Example 1: an off-centre point load

Now, let's look at how the distribution of internal forces along the beam length is calculated. Figure 6.40 shows the free-body diagram of a simply supported beam subjected to an off-centre transverse load W acting in the y-direction. Note that because there is no load component in the x-direction, the horizontal support reactions are zero, so I have drawn only the vertical reactions in the free-body diagram.

SAQ 6.5 (Learning outcome 6.6)

Determine the support reactions of the beam shown in Figure 6.40 in terms of W, a, b and L. (You don't know the values, so just write out the equations ready to plug in the numbers when you know them.)

I have made my first imaginary cut on plane CC′ at a distance x from the left-hand end. Here, x could take any value between 0 and a, the point where the external load is applied. I have drawn the free-body diagram of the left-hand portion of the beam

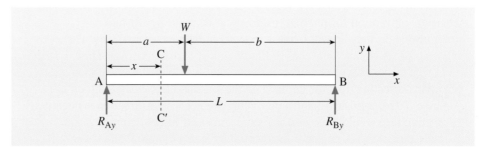

Figure 6.40   Free-body diagram of a simply supported beam with an external point load

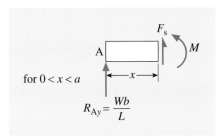

Figure 6.41   Free-body diagram of the cut beam from Figure 6.40, with the cut placed to the left of the point load

in Figure 6.41. I have put the shear force F_s and the bending moment M at the cut face, but I have omitted the axial force F_n, as it should be zero because there is no horizontal load applied to the beam.

I can now determine the internal forces by applying the equilibrium equations. For shear force, summing the forces in the y-direction gives:

$$\sum F_y = 0$$
$$R_{Ay} + F_s = 0$$

Rearranging and substituting $R_{Ay} = Wb/L$ (which you derived in SAQ 6.5):

$$F_s = -\frac{Wb}{L} \tag{6.9}$$

That is, the shear force is equal to the left-hand support reaction, but in the opposite direction. To determine the bending moment at the cut face, I can sum the bending moments about the midpoint of the cut (so that at least one of the forces, in this case F_s, is eliminated from the equation). Taking the anticlockwise rotations as positive:

$$\sum M_A = 0$$
$$M - R_{Ay} x = 0$$

Rearranging and substituting $R_{Ay} = Wb/L$ gives:

$$M = \frac{Wb}{L} x \tag{6.10}$$

Notice that, while the shear force is constant between the left-hand support and the point where the transverse load is applied ($x = a$), the magnitude of the bending moment linearly increases in the same interval, as a function of x. It is perhaps unsurprising that there is a bigger bending moment the further we get from the support.

To find out what happens to the shear force and bending moment on the right-hand side of the external load, I need to make an imaginary cut at a position between the external load and the right-hand support (Figure 6.42).

Applying equilibrium in the y-direction now gives:

$$\frac{Wb}{L} - W + F_s = 0$$

Point loads on beams cause a mathematical discontinuity in the shear-force and bending-moment distribution, and therefore the imaginary cut should not be taken at the plane of the load. The complete distribution can still be determined by analysing the beam in separate free-body diagrams obtained by sectioning the beam either side of the position of the external load and combining the results, as I will show here.

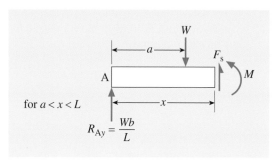

Figure 6.42 Free-body diagram of the beam from Figure 6.40, with the cut placed to the right of the point load

Thus:

$$F_s = \frac{W(L-b)}{L}$$

Since $L - b = a$, I can write this as:

$$F_s = \frac{Wa}{L} \tag{6.11}$$

Thus, the shear force on the right-hand side of the external load is equal to, and in the same direction as, the force at the right-hand support. Taking moments about the cut axis (at $a < x < L$) gives:

$$M + W(x-a) - \frac{Wb}{L}x = 0$$

Rearranging:

$$M = \frac{Wbx}{L} - Wx + Wa$$

$$= \frac{W}{L}\left(bx - Lx + La\right)$$

Rearranging and substituting $b = L - a$ gives:

$$M = \frac{Wa}{L}(L-x) \tag{6.12}$$

Again, the bending moment varies with distance x along the length of the beam. This time it decreases towards the right-hand side; so, as before, it is largest closer to the application point of the load.

Now, I know that this looks like a lot of algebra for its own sake, but you're about to see the pay-off, as we can use the results of the analysis to picture more clearly what's going on within the beam. The easiest way to see the variation of shear force and bending moment is to plot all the results along the length of the beam. I have obtained the shear-force variation along the beam by combining Equations (6.9) and (6.11), and the bending-moment variation from Equations (6.10) and (6.12), and plotted the results in Figure 6.43. Such graphs are called *shear-force and bending-moment diagrams*, and they are important tools in beam design. It is good practice to align the diagrams with the free-body diagram of the beam so that the critical locations on the beam, such as where the forces are maximum or minimum, are immediately visible.

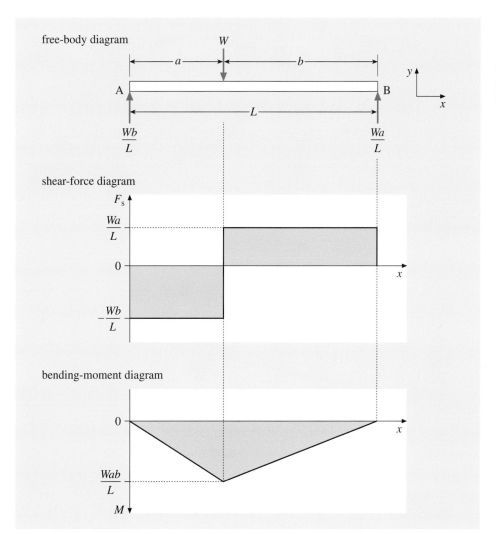

Figure 6.43 Shear-force and bending-moment diagrams for a simply supported beam subject to an off-centre transverse load

Note that I have plotted the bending-moment diagram in Figure 6.43 in a slightly unconventional way: I have drawn the positive axis downwards. It is not uncommon to use this representation, as it is more intuitive when the positive values on the bending-moment diagram are in the same direction as the actual deformation of the beam. That means a positive bending moment causing the beam to sag plots below the beam, and a negative bending moment causing the beam to hog plots above it.

It is worth noting some important points about Figure 6.43. The magnitude of the shear force is negative, but constant, to the left of the point load. Its magnitude changes abruptly at the point load (by the amount of the load) and becomes positive to the right of the load. The bending moment is positive (sagging) throughout the beam, but it varies linearly along the length of the beam, with a sudden change in its slope at the point load, where it reaches its maximum. As expected, the bending moment is zero at both supports.

The simply supported beam with an off-centre point load is one of the basic beam configurations (sometimes referred to as *three-point bending*) that occur in real structures (see Figure 6.44), and hence the results I have obtained for it are regarded as standard and are often used in beam design.

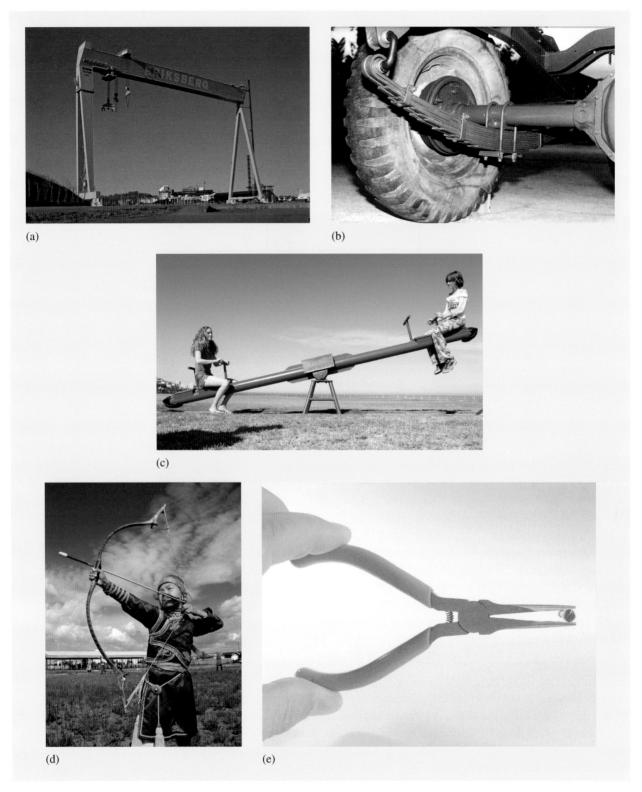

Figure 6.44   Examples of structural members subjected to three-point bending: (a) the horizontal beam of an overhead crane; (b) the leaf-springs of a vehicle suspension; (c) a see-saw; (d) a drawn bow; (e) a pair of pliers in use

We can gather more general information about the reaction of beams to concentrated loads by studying the shear-force and bending-moment diagrams in Figure 6.43. I want you now to look at the diagrams carefully and try to answer Exercise 6.9.

EXERCISE 6.9

You are about to put a very heavy vase on a shelf unit that you have fixed to the wall. The problem is that you are not sure whether the shelf and the fixings, which you can model as a simply supported beam, are strong enough to carry your expensive vase. You would like to position the vase along the shelf such that the risk of the shelf collapsing is decreased.

What position of the vase along the shelf reduces the risk of:

(a) shelf failure by fracture of the beam

(b) fixing (support) failure?

You can assume the weight of the vase as a point load on the shelf.

SAQ 6.6 (Learning outcomes 6.6 and 6.7)

Construct the shear-force and bending-moment diagrams for the simply supported beam subjected to two identical point loads (otherwise known as four-point bending) given in Figure 6.45.

Do this as follows:

(a) Calculate the support reactions.

(b) Take imaginary cuts through the beam, and calculate expressions for the bending moments and shear forces associated with each cut. You will need to take three cuts for a complete description of the forces and moments.

(c) Sketch out the bending-moment and shear-force diagrams as a function of position along the beam.

Hint: this shouldn't be a complex task. Work out values for the ends and the loading points in the first instance, and if you're confident there's a linear variation in between (i.e. the variation is a function of x, not, for example, x^2) you can join up the points using straight lines.

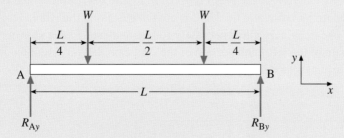

Figure 6.45   Simply supported beam with two identical point loads

The answer to SAQ 6.6 shows that when a beam is loaded in four-point bending, as in Figure 6.45, there is a constant bending moment between the inner supports.

(a)

Figure 6.46   (a) A specimen loaded in four-point bending in a testing machine; (b) a weight-lifting bar is an example of a beam subjected to four-point bending

This makes it a useful configuration when testing materials properties. Figure 6.46(a) shows a bend sample being tested to measure its fatigue and fracture properties.

2.3.4 Example 2: uniformly distributed loads

When determining the reaction forces in beams subjected to UDLs, I simplified the distributed loads by replacing them with equivalent point loads concentrated at the mid-position of the UDL. But clearly care is needed in applying this approximation when the internal forces are determined. The internal force distribution of a beam subjected to a UDL will not show the step changes we have just seen in a beam with a point load; the change will be more gradual. So replacing the UDL with an equivalent point load would, for example, result in incorrect shear-force and bending-moment distributions. However, once the beam is sectioned, the equivalent point load can be used in applying the equilibrium equations to obtain the shear force and bending moment at the cut surface. I will show you how this is done on a simply supported beam with a UDL.

The free-body diagram of the beam is given in Figure 6.47. Since there is no point load applied to the beam and the UDL is continuous along the whole length of the beam, just one imaginary cut is necessary for the analysis. I have shown the free-body diagram of the left-hand portion of the cut beam, length x, and the internal forces at the cut surface in Figure 6.48.

Figure 6.47   Simply supported beam subjected to a UDL

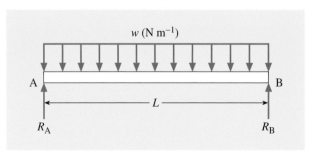

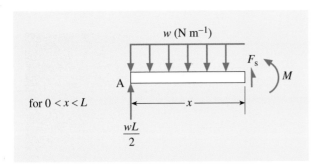

Figure 6.48   Free-body diagram of the left-hand portion of the simply supported beam given in Figure 6.47

Since there is no horizontal load applied to the beam, the axial force F_n at the cut face is zero. The total load carried by the beam is $w \times L$, so the magnitude of both support reactions is $wL/2$.

Note that when I sectioned the beam, I also sectioned the UDL at the same plane. So, the total applied load on the left-hand portion of the beam in Figure 6.48 is $w \times x$. Equilibrium in the y-direction then gives:

$$\frac{wL}{2} + F_s - wx = 0$$

Thus:

$$F_s = wx - \frac{wL}{2} \tag{6.13}$$

As expected, the shear force shows a linear dependence on distance x.

When applying the moment equilibrium, the equivalent point load, $w \times x$, is assumed to act at the mid-position of the UDL, i.e. a distance of $x/2$ to the cut surface. Taking moments about the middle of the cut surface then gives (taking anticlockwise rotations as positive):

$$-\frac{wL}{2} \times x + wx \times \frac{x}{2} + M = 0$$

$$M = \frac{wL}{2}x - \frac{w}{2}x^2 \tag{6.14}$$

The bending-moment function is therefore more complex than we have seen previously, depending on both x and x^2. Both Equations (6.13) and (6.14), for the shear force F_s and the bending moment M, apply right across the span for all values of x, since there are no point loads and the UDL is unbroken.

To construct the shear-force and bending-moment diagrams, we substitute length values between 0 and L for the variable x in the equations. I have plotted them in Figure 6.49, where it is clearly seen that the shear force increases linearly from a negative value at the left-hand support to a positive value at the right-hand support. The bending moment shows a *parabolic* distribution across the beam span. As you might expect, the bending moment is a maximum at the mid-span; substituting $L/2$

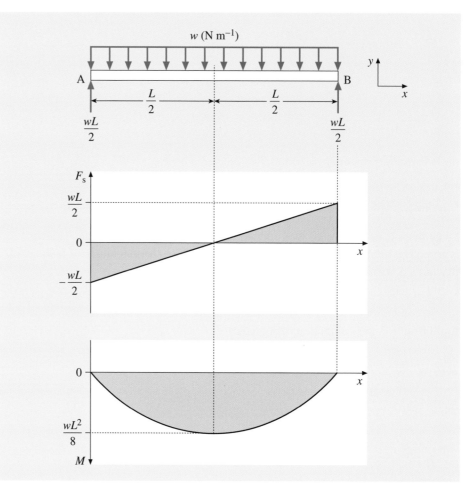

Figure 6.49 Shear-force and bending-moment diagrams for a simply supported beam subject to a UDL

for x in Equation (6.14) gives this as $wL^2/8$. In fact, you don't have to plot the graph to find this: see the input ☑ **Finding the maximum bending moment** ☑.

It is important to make the imaginary cuts at appropriate locations when determining the shear-force and bending-moment distributions. So, what are the 'correct' locations? In general, it is necessary to analyse every point on the beam where there is a change in loading. You saw earlier that the loading on a beam changes at an applied point load, as do the shear-force and bending-moment distributions. Therefore, we need to determine their distributions on both sides of the loading point separately, which means splitting the beam before and after the point load and then applying the equilibrium conditions to determine equations for shear force and bending moment for both cuts. Note that support reactions have the same effect as point loads on the distributions of shear force and bending moment, so they should be treated as point loads when analysing the beams. Therefore, if supports are positioned not at the ends of a beam, but further in (leaving hanging ends), then imaginary cuts should be made at both sides of the support.

▽ Finding the maximum bending moment

Since the simply supported beam subjected to a UDL is a symmetrical case, it is clear that the maximum bending moment should occur at mid-span. But for non-symmetrical cases this may not be so obvious, so we turn to differential calculus for help. (If you can follow the discussion here, fine. Don't worry if you can't, as you won't have to reproduce it.)

The derivative (or differential) of a function gives the slope of the function. Since at a maximum (or minimum) of a function the slope becomes zero, differentiating the bending-moment equation (e.g. Equation 6.14) and equating it to zero gives the position of maximum bending moment along the beam. We can check whether the mid-span position was really where the maximum bending moment occurs in the above problem by differentiating Equation (6.14):

$$M = \frac{wL}{2}x - \frac{w}{2}x^2$$

$$\frac{dM}{dx} = \frac{wL}{2} - wx$$

So, setting $dM/dx = 0$ gives:

$$\frac{wL}{2} - wx = 0$$

Therefore:

$$x = \frac{L}{2}$$

As expected, the maximum bending moment indeed occurs at mid-span. ◩

2.3.5 Example 3: non-continuous uniformly distributed loads

Apart from concentrated loads, *broken* (or *non-continuous*) UDLs (i.e. UDLs that do not run continuously along the whole length of the beam) cause a sudden change in loading at the positions where they start and finish. Consequently, the shear force and bending moments need to be determined before and after this change. I will demonstrate how this is done with another example.

EXAMPLE

A person climbing a ladder applies a load of 900 N on a ladder rung, as shown in Figure 6.50. If the load is uniformly distributed along the width of the shoe, determine the internal force distribution in the ladder rung and find the maximum bending moment. What would be the maximum bending moment if the whole load were concentrated at the centre of distributed load? You can idealize the rung as a simply supported beam and you can neglect its self-weight.

Figure 6.50   A foot on a ladder rung

SOLUTION

As usual, I simplify the problem. I assume that the ladder rung was a simply supported beam. In reality, the rungs in a ladder are usually fixed to the side rails in reasonably rigid joints. This configuration (a beam with both ends built in) would make it statically indeterminate, and we could not find a solution with the techniques we have learned so far. However, the treatment of the rung as a simply supported beam makes good engineering sense when the purpose of the analysis is to investigate the structural integrity of the rung. The maximum bending moment developed in a simply supported beam is much higher (as much as three times) than that of a beam built in at both ends, because the built-in ends would bear that portion of the bending moment developed due to transverse loading. So, a simply supported beam represents the worst case as far as the failure of the rung due to bending is concerned.

I have drawn the free-body diagram of the rung as a simply supported beam in Figure 6.51. The UDL exerted by the foot is the total load divided by the shoe width, i.e. 900 N/0.1 m, which is 9000 N m^{-1}. The support reactions are found in the usual way. First, taking moments about A:

$$-9000 \text{ N m}^{-1} \times 0.1 \text{ m} \times 0.23 \text{ m} + R_B \times 0.35 \text{ m} = 0$$

Figure 6.51   Free-body diagram of a foot on a ladder rung

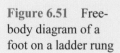

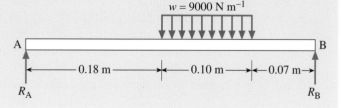

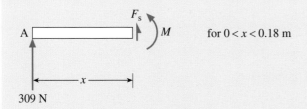

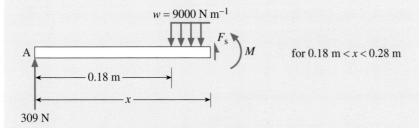

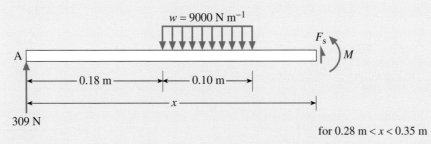

Figure 6.52   Free-body diagrams for the three cuts in the beam

Therefore:

$$R_B = 591 \text{ N}$$

Equilibrium in the y-direction gives:

$$-9000 \text{ N m}^{-1} \times 0.1 \text{ m} + R_B + R_A = 0$$

Thus:

$$R_A = 309 \text{ N}$$

Now, I can make my imaginary cuts to determine the internal forces. There are three regions with distinct loading: (1) the region between the left-hand support and the point where the UDL starts; (2) the UDL; (3) the region between the UDL and the right-hand support. So, I have to make three cuts to the beam, as shown in Figure 6.52. Applying the equilibrium conditions to each free-body diagram gives:

1   For $0 < x < 0.18 \text{ m}$

Equilibrium in the y-direction gives:

$$309 \text{ N} + F_S = 0$$

Therefore:

$$F_S = -309 \text{ N}$$

Taking moments about the cut face:

$$-309 \text{ N} \times x + M = 0$$

so

$$M = (309x) \text{ N m}$$

2   For 0.18 m $< x <$ 0.28 m

Equilibrium in the y-direction gives:

$$309 - 9000 \times (x - 0.18) + F_S = 0$$

Thus:

$$F_S = (9000x - 1929) \text{ N}$$

Taking moments about the cut face:

$$-309 \times x + 9000 \times (x - 0.18) \times \frac{x - 0.18}{2} + M = 0$$

so

$$M = 309x - \frac{9000}{2}(x - 0.18)(x - 0.18)$$
$$= (-4500x^2 + 1929x - 145.8) \text{ N m}$$

3   For 0.28 m $< x <$ 0.35 m

Equilibrium in the y-direction gives:

$$309 \text{ N} - 9000 \text{ N m}^{-1} \times 0.1 \text{ m} + F_S = 0$$

so

$$F_S = 591 \text{ N}$$

Taking moments about the cut face:

$$-309 \times x + 9000 \times 0.10 \times (x - 0.23) + M = 0$$

Therefore:

$$M = (-591x + 207) \text{ N m}$$

It's now a matter of plotting the shear-force and bending-moment diagrams by substituting for x at various lengths between 0 m and 0.35 m into the equations determined above. The diagrams are shown in Figure 6.53.

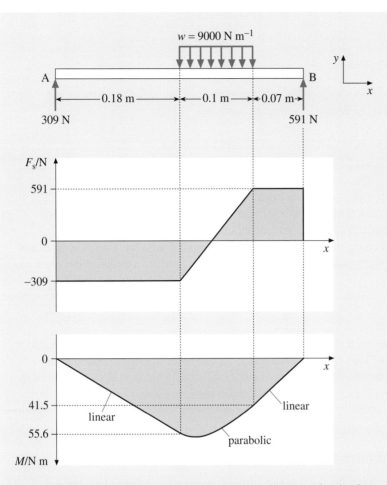

Figure 6.53 Shear-force and bending-moment diagrams for the foot-on-a-ladder-rung example

The magnitude of the maximum bending moment and the exact position along the beam where it occurs cannot be read from the diagram, although it is obvious that it should be in the region where the UDL is applied.
I can determine the exact location by the method I described earlier, i.e. by differentiating the bending-moment equation for the UDL region (for 0.18 m $<$ x $<$ 0.28 m):

$$M = -4500x^2 + 1929x - 145.8$$

$$\frac{\mathrm{d}M}{\mathrm{d}x} = -9000x + 1929$$

which gives the slope of the bending-moment diagram at every value of x. Since the slope is zero at the maximum of the curve, equating the above equation to zero would give us the location where the bending moment is the maximum. So:

$$-9000x + 1929 = 0$$

Thus:

$$x = 0.214 \text{ m}$$

The magnitude of the maximum bending moment is found by substituting $x = 0.214$ into the bending-moment equation:

$$M_{max} = -4500 \times 0.214^2 + 1929 \times 0.214 - 145.8$$
$$= 60.9 \text{ N m}$$

What would be the maximum bending moment if the whole load were concentrated at the centre of distributed load? I can calculate this easily by using the standard solution that I obtained earlier (see Figure 6.43). The maximum bending moment occurs at the location where the load is applied and has the following magnitude:

$$M_{max} = \frac{Wab}{L}$$

If I substitute the total load $W = 900$ N, the distances from the left-hand support to the point of load application $a = 0.23$ m and from the right-hand support $b = 0.12$ m, and the beam length L = 0.35 m, then I calculate M_{max} as 70.9 N m, which is significantly higher than the case where the load is applied as a UDL.

SAQ 6.7 (Learning outcomes 6.1 and 6.3)

The ladder rung in the previous example is made of an aluminium, hollow square section with the dimensions shown in Figure 6.54. When calculating the second moment of area of the section you can ignore the rounding of the corners.

Calculate the maximum stress in the rung if the load applied by the user's foot is:

(a) uniformly distributed as in Figure 6.50

(b) concentrated at the centre of distributed load.

Assume that the foot applies the load on the top face of the rung evenly and vertically in each case.

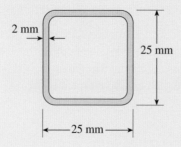

2 mm

25 mm

25 mm

Figure 6.54   Cross section of an aluminium ladder rung

SAQ 6.8 (Learning outcomes 6.1 and 6.3)

A ladder manufacturer wants to use solid timber with a circular cross section for rungs in an all-timber ladder (Figure 6.55). The design load for the rung is 175 kg.

Calculate the minimum diameter for the rungs for the design loading case if the maximum allowable stress for the timber is 70 MPa. Repeat your calculations incorporating a load factor of 2. Use 'worst case' loading, which means treating the rung as a simply supported beam with the entire load concentrated at the middle of the rung.

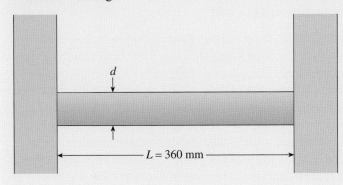

Figure 6.55 A ladder rung made of timber

2.3.6 Combinations of loads

So far we have looked at cases where the loading on beams was either concentrated or uniformly distributed. As you might imagine, beams in real structures are often subjected to a combination of both types of loading. The analysis of such cases is no different from the 'cut and equilibrate' method that we have used above. You may just have to deal with more imaginary cuts and lengthy equilibrium equations due to additional external loads, that's all! In practice, such problems are usually analysed by computer, using either precisely the methodology developed here or, for more complex problems, deflection-based or finite element methods.

Now try the following SAQ.

SAQ 6.9 (Learning outcomes 6.6 and 6.7)

Sketch the shear-force and bending-moment diagrams for a simply supported beam subjected to a point load at its centre and a UDL, as shown in Figure 6.56.

Compare the diagrams with those for the simply supported beams subjected to a point load only and a UDL only, given in Figures 6.43 and 6.49, and comment on the similarities between them.

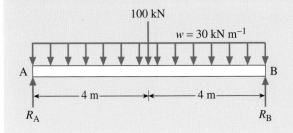

Figure 6.56 Simply supported beam subjected to a point load and a UDL

When dealing with linear elastic structures subjected to complex loading conditions, it is possible to split the loading into simpler cases and to sum the solutions. This is known as the *principle of superposition*, a method used widely in mechanics to analyse a complex loading condition on a quantity such as force, displacement, strain, etc. We have already used this important principle in Part 2 of this block to calculate the strain caused by complex stress states.

So, SAQ 6.9 could have been solved by combining the solutions for a beam subjected to a point load and a beam subjected to a UDL. In fact, we have already obtained solutions to these separate cases earlier; Figure 6.43 shows the shear-force and bending-moment diagrams for a beam subjected to a point load, and Figure 6.49 shows the same for a beam subjected to a UDL.

Let me demonstrate the validity of the principle of superposition by finding the maximum bending moment in the beam given in Figure 6.56. First consider the point load, 100 kN, applied at mid-span. The solution in Figure 6.43 gives the maximum bending moment as Wab/L, which gives (with $a = b = 4$ m and $L = 8$ m) 200 kN m. The maximum bending moment for a beam subjected to a UDL only is shown in Figure 6.49 as $wL^2/8$, and for $w = 30$ kN m^{-1} this comes to 240 kN m. The maximum bending moment for the combined loading should then be the summation of the individual maximums, i.e. 200 kN m + 240 kN m = 440 kN m, which agrees with the solution obtained using the 'cut and equilibrate' method in SAQ 6.9.

In fact, not just a single value but the whole of the shear-force and bending-moment diagrams can be obtained by this method. This is what I have done in Figure 6.57; I have taken the individual shear-force and bending-moment diagrams for a point load and a UDL, and summed the diagrams to get the total effect when both loads are applied simultaneously.

The use of the principle of superposition is practical only when the problem can be split into known standard configurations. Two more standard beam solutions are shown in Figure 6.58 for cantilevers subjected to a concentrated load at the free end and a UDL respectively. The methods we have used in the analysis of simply supported beams are fully applicable to cantilevers. The main difference between the two types of beam is that there is a bending-moment reaction at the built-in support in a cantilever, in addition to vertical and horizontal reaction forces. Although they can be drawn either way, here I have drawn the built-in ends of the cantilevers on the right, because it is more convenient to start x from the left-hand side when applying the 'cut and equilibrate' method.

EXERCISE 6.10

A diver weighing 750 N stands at the free end of a 3 m long diving board. Using Figure 6.58, calculate the reaction forces at the built-in end of the platform if the self-weight of the board is 160 N m^{-1}. What is the magnitude and where is the location of the maximum bending moment in the board?

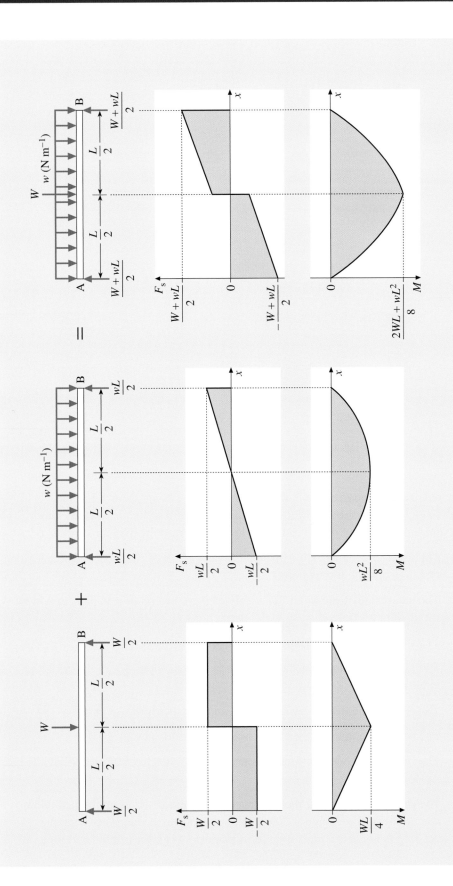

Figure 6.57 The use of the principle of superposition to find solutions to combined loading

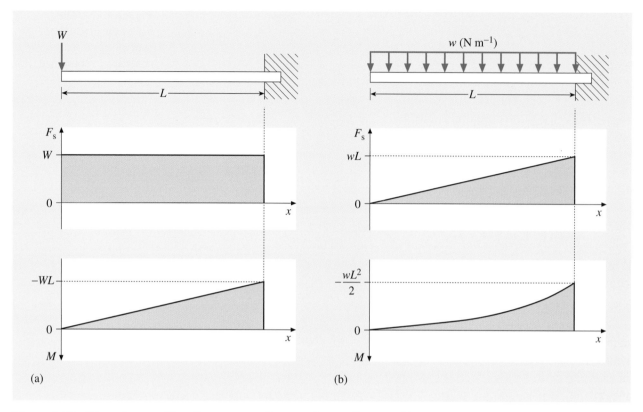

Figure 6.58 Shear-force and bending-moment diagrams for cantilevers subjected to (a) a point load at the free end and (b) a UDL

There are a few important points worth summarizing about shear-force and bending-moment diagrams, which you may find useful when analysing beams. You may already have observed them when you plotted the diagrams earlier.

1   The shear force in a beam with a point load only is constant between the loading points (including the supports).

2   The magnitude of shear force suddenly changes at a point load or a support by the amount of the load or the support reaction.

3   The shear force along a UDL varies linearly.

4   The positive bending moments are always drawn on the side of the beam that is in tension.

5   The bending moment in a beam with a point load only varies linearly.

6   The bending moment shows a parabolic distribution along a UDL.

7   The slope of the bending-moment curve changes at a loading point (including at supports).

8   The slope of the bending-moment curve at a point in the beam is equal to the magnitude of shear force at that point, but opposite in sign. Therefore, the bending moment is a maximum (or minimum) when shear force is zero.

2.4 Shear stresses in beams

You saw in the previous section that beams generally (with the exception of the case of pure bending) have a shear force F_s acting in any given transverse section of the beam, as shown in Figure 6.59(a). This shear force generates shear stresses on the vertical section of the beam. These shear stresses are not constant from the top to the bottom of the section, but they are assumed to be constant across the width of the section (in the z-direction) for all practical purposes. At all points in the beam, the shear stresses in the vertical direction (τ_{xy} in Figure 6.59b) are accompanied by the complementary shear stresses in the horizontal direction, i.e. τ_{yx}. Furthermore, since we are studying only the cases where all the loads are on the xy-plane, there are no shear forces in the z-direction, so all the shear stresses in this direction (i.e. τ_{xz}, τ_{zx}, τ_{yz}, τ_{zy}) should be zero.

The derivation of shear stresses in bending is rather complex, so I'm going to skip it in this course. However, I will show you here how the shear stresses vary in two common beam sections.

First, Figure 6.60 shows the generic distribution of shear stress through a beam with a rectangular cross section. The shear stress shows a parabolic distribution across the section; it is zero at the top and the bottom edges of the beam and maximum at the neutral axis. Hence, it is a useful rule of thumb to remember that the bending moment in a beam is carried by forces at the top and bottom, but the shear is carried by the material near the neutral plane.

The maximum shear stress at the neutral surface for a rectangular cross section is found to be given by:

$$\tau_{max} = \frac{F_s h^2}{8 I_z} \tag{6.15}$$

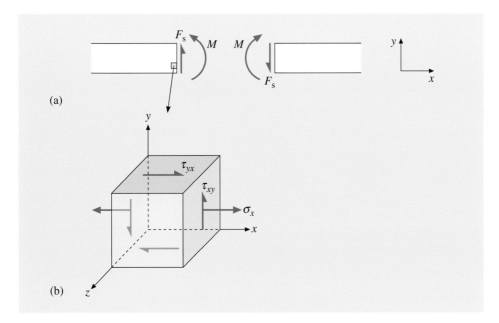

(a)

(b)

Figure 6.59 (a) Internal forces and (b) the resulting stresses in a beam under general loading

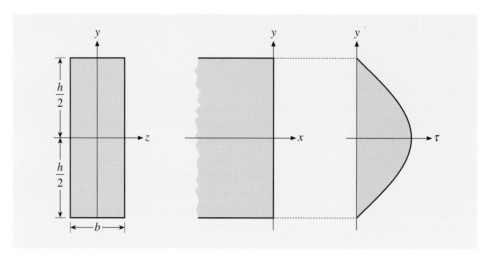

Figure 6.60   Shear stress distribution through a beam with rectangular cross section

where F_s is the shear force in the section, h is the height of the beam and I_z is the second moment of the area of the section about the z-axis.

A more complex distribution is seen in an I-beam, as you might expect. The shear stress distribution in an I-beam consists of two different distributions (Figure 6.61): one for the web section and one for each flange section. The greatest shear stress occurs at the neutral axis of the beam, which is much bigger, relatively, than the shear stress in the flanges. For design purposes, the web is assumed to resist all the shear forces, and the flanges to resist the bending forces. It is found that the maximum shear stress in an I-beam may be estimated reasonably accurately by dividing the shear force by the area of the web:

$$\tau_{max} = \frac{F_s}{A_{web}} \tag{6.16}$$

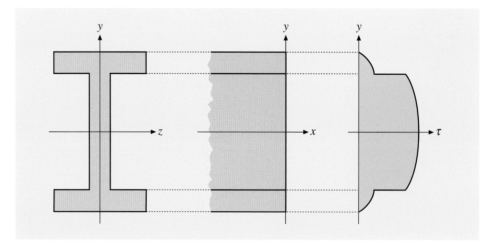

Figure 6.61   Shear stress distribution through an I-beam section

EXAMPLE

Estimate the magnitude and the location of the maximum longitudinal and shear stresses in a cantilever with a rectangular cross section, as shown in Figure 6.62, subjected to a point load of 30 kN.

Compare the stresses.

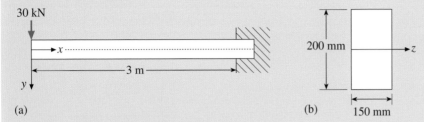

(a)   (b)

Figure 6.62   Cantilever with a rectangular cross section, subjected to a point load at its end

SOLUTION

From the shear-force diagram for a cantilever in Figure 6.58(a), recall that the shear force is constant along the length of the beam with a magnitude equal to the applied load, ignoring the self-weight of the beam. The second moment of area of the beam is:

$$I_z = \frac{bh^3}{12} = \frac{0.15 \text{ m} \times (0.2 \text{ m})^3}{12} = 1.00 \times 10^{-4} \text{ m}^4$$

The maximum shear stress in the beam is given by Equation (6.15):

$$\tau_{max} = \frac{F_s h^2}{8 I_z} = \frac{30 \times 10^3 \text{ N} \times (0.2 \text{ m})^2}{8 \times 1.00 \times 10^{-4} \text{ m}^4} = 1.5 \times 10^6 \text{ Pa} = 1.5 \text{ MPa}$$

Then, again from Figure 6.58(a), we recall that the maximum bending moment occurs at the built-in end with a magnitude of $M_{max} = WL$. For the rectangular section, the maximum bending stress is then:

$$\sigma_{max} = \frac{M_{max} y}{I_z} = \frac{(30 \times 10^3 \text{ N} \times 3 \text{ m}) \times (0.2 \text{ m}/2)}{1.00 \times 10^{-4} \text{ m}^4} = 90 \times 10^6 \text{ Pa} = 90 \text{ MPa}$$

which is significantly higher than the maximum shear stress.

SAQ 6.10 (Learning outcomes 6.1, 6.3 and 6.8)

Repeat the calculations shown in the previous example for the I-beam section shown in Figure 6.63.

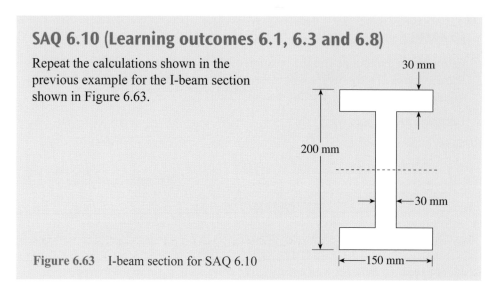

30 mm

200 mm

30 mm

150 mm

Figure 6.63   I-beam section for SAQ 6.10

As the example and SAQ 6.10 demonstrate, the shear stresses in beams are generally an order of magnitude smaller than the longitudinal bending stresses; and thus, together with the fact that they are concentrated away from the areas in which the bending stresses are largest for a given cross section, we do not often consider them at the early stages of designing a beam. Therefore, we need only to design a beam to carry the maximum bending stresses at the section where the bending moment is a maximum.

2.5 Combined bending and axial loading

In practice, structural members are often subjected to bending and axial loads simultaneously. Figures 6.64(a) and (b) show two simple examples where the loading in each case causes the general set of internal forces shown in Figure 6.64(c). As you learned earlier in this part, the transverse load F_1 in Figure 6.64(a), or the vertical component (with respect to the beam's longitudinal axis) of the inclined force F in Figure 6.64(b), generates a bending moment M and a shear force F_s in the beam. There is also now an axial force F_n in the beam, but this is simply equal to the direct axial load F_2 in Figure 6.64(a) or the horizontal component of F in Figure 6.64(b).

Figure 6.64   Examples of general modes of loading beams: (a) a cantilever subjected to a transverse and an axial load; (b) a simply supported beam subjected to an inclined transverse load; (c) the resulting internal forces at a section of the beam

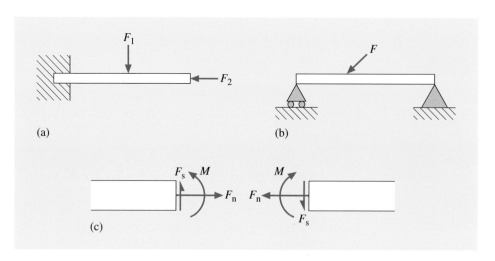

The stresses associated with these internal forces can be determined by applying the appropriate methods that you have learned so far. Whereas the shear force F_s gives rise to shear stresses, both the bending moment M and the axial force F_n cause longitudinal stresses in the beam. For now, I want to ignore the shear stresses as they are not affected by the presence of axial loads, nor do they have any influence on longitudinal stresses. What I am interested in is the longitudinal stresses caused by the bending moment and the axial force, since they act together on the beam and their combined effect should be considered to determine the magnitude and direction of the total stress in the section.

Look at Figure 6.65(a), which shows a beam subjected to a bending moment and an axial force. The bending moment produces a linearly varying stress $\sigma_x = My/I_z$ through the section, as shown in Figure 6.65(b), with compressive stresses at the upper section of the beam and tensile stresses at the lower section. The axial force produces a uniform stress in the section, equal to the axial force divided by the cross-sectional area of the beam, i.e. $\sigma_x = F_n/A$, which is taken as positive (i.e. tensile) in this example, as shown in Figure 6.65(c). The combined (or *net*) stress at any point can be simply obtained by the algebraic sum of the individual stresses at that point (yet another example of the principle of superposition):

$$\sigma_x = \frac{F_n}{A} + \frac{My}{I_z} \qquad (6.17)$$

Care should be taken to use the correct signs for the stress terms when carrying out the summation. This is straightforward for the first stress term F_n/A: it is positive when the axial force F_n is tensile and it is negative when F_n is compressive. However, the sign of the bending stress term My/I_z depends on whether the point of interest is on the upper or lower part of the beam and on the sign of the bending moment M. I set my sign convention for bending moment such that a positive M produces compressive (negative) stresses at the upper part of the beam and tensile (positive) stresses at the lower part of the beam, as in the case shown in Figure 6.65(b). A convenient way of making sure that the bending stress term has the correct sign is to take y (the distance from the neutral axis) as negative in the upper part of the beam and positive in the lower part, which is how I have drawn the reference frame shown in Figure 6.65.

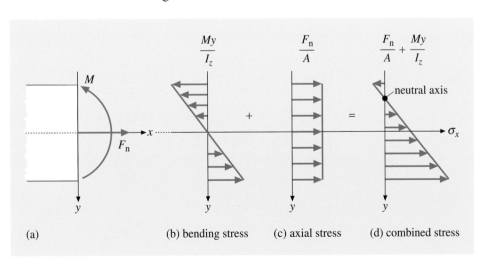

(a) (b) bending stress (c) axial stress (d) combined stress

Figure 6.65 The distribution of longitudinal stresses in a beam subjected to combined bending and axial loads: (a) bending moment and axial force at a cut through the beam; (b) bending stress distribution through the thickness of the beam; (c) longitudinal stresses due to the axial force; (d) combined stress distribution

Perhaps the easiest way of determining the combined stress is to carry out the summation graphically, as shown in Figure 6.65. You may already have noticed that the slope of the combined stress distribution (Figure 6.65d) is the same as the bending stress distribution (Figure 6.65b). Thus, the combined stress distribution can be obtained by shifting the bending stress distribution by an amount equal to the axial stress term.

An important consequence of combined bending and axial loads is that the neutral axis, i.e. the axis where the longitudinal stress is zero, is no longer coincident with the centroidal axis of the beam, as in the example given in Figure 6.65(d). Of course, the combined stress distribution depends on the relative magnitudes and directions of the individual stresses involved; hence, the position of the neutral axis can be anywhere on the cross section or, indeed, it may fall outside the cross section (meaning that there is no longer a zero-stress point inside the beam) when the combined stress distribution is tensile or compressive throughout the section. We can easily find the position of the neutral axis with respect to the centroidal axis of the cross section: since the longitudinal stress is zero at the neutral axis, setting $\sigma_x = 0$ in Equation (6.17) and solving for y gives the distance between the neutral axis and the centroidal axis of the cross section:

$$y_{na} = -\frac{F_n I_z}{AM} \tag{6.18}$$

EXAMPLE

The cantilever I-beam shown in Figure 6.66 is subjected to an inclined force of 100 kN acting through the centroidal axis of the cross section. Calculate the maximum longitudinal stress in the beam and the position of the neutral axis with respect to the centroidal axis.

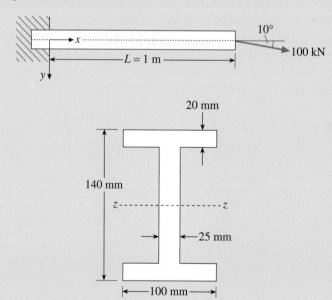

Figure 6.66   A cantilever subjected to an inclined end force

SOLUTION

First, it is helpful to resolve the applied force into its horizontal and vertical components (Figure 6.67a) and determine the resulting internal forces at the beam's cross section (Figure 6.67b). Since I am interested only in the longitudinal stresses in the beam, I have omitted the shear force in the figure and shown only the axial force and the bending moment.

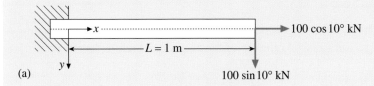

(a)

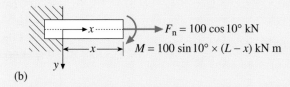

(b)

Figure 6.67 (a) Components of the applied force; (b) internal forces at a section that will cause longitudinal stresses (i.e. shear force is ignored)

The axial force gives rise to a longitudinal stress that is constant through the length of the beam:

$$\sigma_x = \frac{F_n}{A}$$

$$= \frac{100 \times 10^3 \text{ N} \times \cos 10°}{2 \times (100 \times 10^{-3} \text{ m} \times 20 \times 10^{-3} \text{ m}) + (100 \times 10^{-3} \text{ m} \times 25 \times 10^{-3} \text{ m})}$$

$$= 15.15 \times 10^6 \text{ Pa}$$

$$= 15.15 \text{ MPa}$$

Recall from Figure 6.58(a) that the bending moment is zero at the free end of the cantilever and at its maximum at the fixed (built-in) end of the beam. It seems that the fixed end is the critical location, where the combined stress would be at a maximum. The magnitude of the maximum bending moment is:

$$M_{max} = -100 \times 10^3 \text{ N} \times \sin 10° \times 1 \text{ m} = -17\,365 \text{ N m}$$

Note that this is a negative bending moment according to our sign convention, as it makes the cantilever hog (see Figure 6.39). To calculate the bending stress, I first need to determine the second moment of area of our I-beam. Using the formula given in Table 6.1:

$$I_z = \frac{bh^3}{12} - 2\frac{cd^3}{12}$$

$$= \frac{100 \times 10^{-3} \text{ m} \times (140 \times 10^{-3} \text{ m})^3}{12} - 2 \times \frac{37.5 \times 10^{-3} \text{ m} \times (100 \times 10^{-3} \text{ m})^3}{12}$$

$$= 1.662 \times 10^{-5} \text{ m}^4$$

The maximum bending stress occurs at the fixed end and at the outermost parts of the section where $y = \pm 70$ mm, thus:

$$\sigma_x = \frac{M_{max}\, y}{I_z} = \frac{-17\,365 \text{ N m} \times (\pm 70 \times 10^{-3} \text{ m})}{1.662 \times 10^{-5} \text{ m}}$$

$$= \pm 73.15 \times 10^6 \text{ Pa}$$

$$= \pm 73.15 \text{ MPa}$$

The combined longitudinal stresses can then be obtained by adding the bending stress and direct axial stress. At the top of the beam, the stress is tensile with a magnitude of $15.15 + 73.15 = 88.3$ MPa, whereas it is compressive at the bottom edge of the beam with a magnitude of $15.15 - 73.15 = -58$ MPa, as shown graphically in Figure 6.68. The shift in the neutral axis can be calculated using Equation (6.18):

$$y_{na} = -\frac{F I_z}{A M} = \frac{10 \times 10^3 \text{ N} \times \cos 10° \times 1.662 \times 10^{-5} \text{ m}^4}{6.5 \times 10^{-3} \text{ m}^2 \times -17\,365 \text{ N m}} = 14.5 \times 10^{-3} \text{ m} = 14.5 \text{ mm}$$

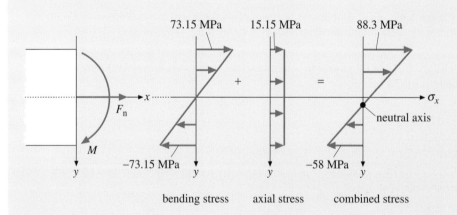

Figure 6.68   The use of the principle of superposition to determine the distribution of the combined stresses in the cantilever shown in Figure 6.66

SAQ 6.11 (Learning outcomes 6.1, 6.3 and 6.6)

The design of the wooden park bench shown in Figure 6.69(a) comprises a set of seating boards supported by two pairs of cantilevers. The vertical supports at each end are fixed into the ground by concrete, and the horizontal cantilevers, onto which the seating boards are attached, are firmly fixed into the vertical supports. The bench is designed to carry a total mass of 360 kg, which may be assumed to be equally shared by each support.

Assuming that the design of the bench's supports and the weight distribution can be simplified as shown in Figure 6.69(b), verify that the maximum stress in the horizontal cantilever does not exceed 67 MPa, which is the maximum allowable bending stress for teak.

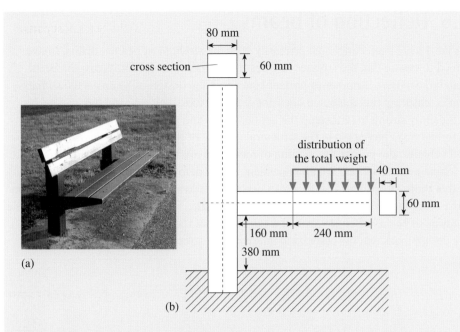

Figure 6.69   (a) A wooden park bench; (b) schematic of one of its supports and design load (side view)

SAQ 6.12 (Learning outcomes 6.1, 6.3, 6.6 and 6.9)

It is also possible to calculate the stresses in the vertical supports in Figure 6.69, which are the second set of cantilevers, although the assumptions are less intuitive and you need to think carefully about how the load is transferred and balanced. The weight does not act directly on this cantilever, but is transferred through the horizontal support. Figure 6.70 shows the loading on the vertical support. Calculate the stress as a result of these loading components.

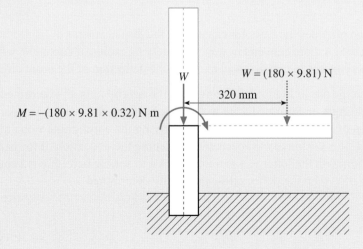

Figure 6.70   Forces on one of the vertical supports of the park bench

2.6 Deflection of beams

So far, I have been concerned primarily with the *strength* of beams: that is, I have aimed to ensure that the stresses in a beam remain within the limits that the beam material can bear. Another important concept in the design of beams is the *stiffness*, that is, ensuring that the beam does not deform excessively. A structure can be sufficiently strong to withstand the applied loads and yet still fail due to excessive deformation (Figure 6.71). The structural rigidity of buildings, mechanical frames and vehicles, the proper functioning of machine parts and the tendency for some machine parts to vibrate are all dependent on the deformation of beam elements within those structures. This is why a maximum allowable deformation or deflection for a beam under a given loading is usually included in a design specification. So, the analysis of beams often involves the calculation of their *maximum deflection* under the design loads and the associated internal peak stresses.

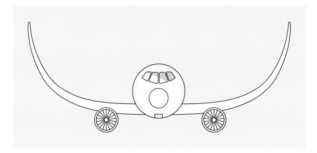

Figure 6.71   Failure does not have to involve fracture

As a matter of fact, the engineer's bending equation does already describe the deformation of a beam subjected to a bending moment, in terms of radius of curvature R; i.e. rearranging Equation (6.6) gives:

$$\frac{M}{EI} = \frac{1}{R} \tag{6.19}$$

This equation provides the basis for calculating the displacements of loaded beams. What we need is a more convenient way of expressing radius of curvature, which is a fairly useless concept in practice, and to obtain the deflection of the beam directly.

Suppose that the arc in Figure 6.72 represents the neutral axis of a deformed beam, which in its undeformed state would just lie along the x-axis. Any particular cross section of the beam can be specified by giving the appropriate value of the coordinate x. It is customary in mechanics to denote the deflection of the beam in the y-direction with the letter v, a practice that I will follow here. If v is known for every value of x, then the deflected shape is fully determined.

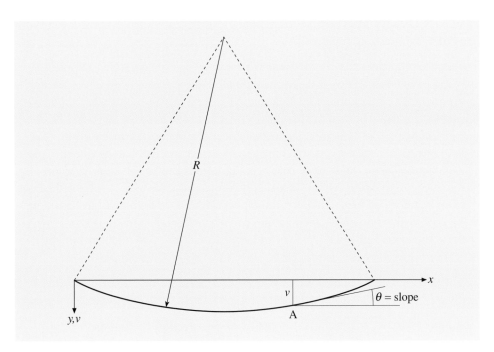

Figure 6.72   Geometry of a bent beam

I will not show the derivation here, but it can be found by analysing the geometry that, when the deflections are small (such as are typically observed in engineering structures), the radius of curvature R is related to the beam deflection v through a second-order differential equation:

$$\frac{1}{R} = -\frac{d^2v}{dx^2}$$

If I substitute for $1/R$ in Equation (6.19) I obtain:

$$\frac{d^2v}{dx^2} = -\frac{M}{EI} \tag{6.20}$$

This equation can be used to determine the deflected shape of any beam, as long as the distribution of the applied bending moment M is known. The product of the elastic modulus and the second moment of area of the section (EI) is known as the *bending stiffness* of the beam (also referred to as *flexural stiffness* or *flexural rigidity*).

The d^2v/dx^2 and M terms in Equation (6.20) represent the curvature and bending moment at a typical point, say A in Figure 6.72, of the beam's axis. If the bending moment at the given point is known, then Equation (6.20) can be integrated twice with respect to x and the deflection v at that point determined. Note that, whereas the second differential of v with respect to x, i.e. d^2v/dx^2, gives the curvature at a given point on the beam's axis, its first differential, i.e. dv/dx, gives the *slope* of the curve at that point, as shown in Figure 6.72.

The input ☑ **Deflection of a cantilever with a point load** ☑ gives an example, showing how the deflection is determined by integrating Equation (6.20). Although it is important that you gain a basic understanding of the capabilities of the technique, it is tedious in many cases and, therefore, you will not be asked to carry out the direct integration method to determine the beam deflections in this course. Besides, we are usually interested in the *maximum deflection* of a beam, rather than its whole shape. The maximum deflection in basic beam configurations can be found in standard tables, such as the one given in Table 6.2. It is often possible to obtain the deflection of more complicated loading configurations by using the principle of superposition; that is, by breaking down the loading into two or more simpler configurations, such as those shown in Table 6.2, and then adding each deflection to find the combined deflection. How to do this in practice is best illustrated by an example.

Table 6.2 Maximum deflection formulae for basic beam configurations

Configuration	Maximum deflection	Position
	$\dfrac{WL^3}{3EI}$	at the free end
	$\dfrac{wL^4}{8EI}$	at the free end
	$\dfrac{WL^3}{48EI}$	at the mid-position
	$\dfrac{5wL^4}{384EI}$	at the mid-position

☑ Deflection of a cantilever with a point load

A cantilever loaded at its free end by a point load is shown in Figure 6.73(a). To find its deflection, I need first to express the distribution of the bending moment M along its length. Making an imaginary cut at a distance x from the free end of the beam and balancing the moments about the cut surface in the free-body diagram in Figure 6.73(b) gives the expression we need:

$$M = -Wx$$

The bending moment is a linear function of x, reaching its maximum at the built-in end (Figure 6.73c). Substituting for M in Equation (6.20) I get:

$$\frac{d^2v}{dx^2} = -\frac{M}{EI} = -\frac{(-Wx)}{EI} = \frac{W}{EI}x$$

Integrating once with respect to x gives:

$$\frac{dv}{dx} = \frac{W}{EI}\left(\frac{x^2}{2} + C_1\right)$$

where C_1 is the constant of integration. A second integration gives:

$$v = \frac{W}{EI}\left(\frac{x^3}{6} + C_1 x + C_2\right)$$

The two constants of integration, C_1 and C_2, can be found using the boundary conditions of the problem. In this case, both of the necessary conditions relate to the built-in end, $x = L$. At this end, both the deflection v and the slope $\theta = dv/dx$ must be zero. (For beams on simple supports, the requisite conditions are that the deflection must be zero at each support).

Beginning with the condition on the slope, I put $dv/dx = 0$ when $x = L$:

$$\left.\frac{dv}{dx}\right|_{x=L} = 0 = \frac{W}{EI}\left(\frac{L^2}{2} + C_1\right)$$

from which I obtain $C_1 = -L^2/2$.

The condition on the deflection at the built-in end is $v = 0$ when $x = L$. Setting $x = L$ in the expression for the deflection, and at the same time putting in the value I have found for C_1, gives:

$$\left.v\right|_{x=L} = 0 = \frac{W}{EI}\left(\frac{L^3}{6} - \frac{L^2}{2}L + C_2\right)$$

We thus find that $C_2 = L^3/3$.

The general expression for the deflection is thus obtained as:

$$v = \frac{WL^3}{EI}\left[\frac{1}{6}\left(\frac{x}{L}\right)^3 - \frac{1}{2}\left(\frac{x}{L}\right) + \frac{1}{3}\right]$$

The deflected form of the beam is sketched in Figure 6.73(d).

The maximum deflection v_{max} occurs at the free end of the beam when $x = 0$:

$$v_{max} = \frac{WL^3}{3EI}$$

which is the same as the formula given in Table 6.2.

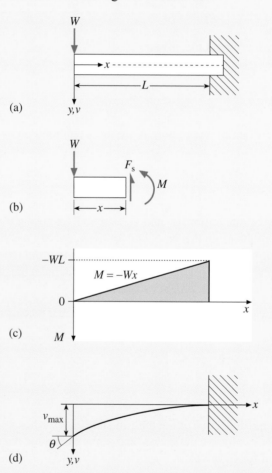

Figure 6.73 Deflection of a cantilever: (a) the loading configuration; (b) the free-body diagram of a section used to determine the bending-moment distribution; (c) the bending-moment diagram; (d) deflected form of the beam (note that the displacements are greatly exaggerated)

EXAMPLE

A 7 m long I-beam made of mild steel is used to support an overhead crane in a workshop, as shown in Figure 6.74. Calculate the maximum deflection when the crane is exactly at the middle of the beam and applying a force of 100 kN on the beam. The elastic modulus of the mild steel is 210 GPa.

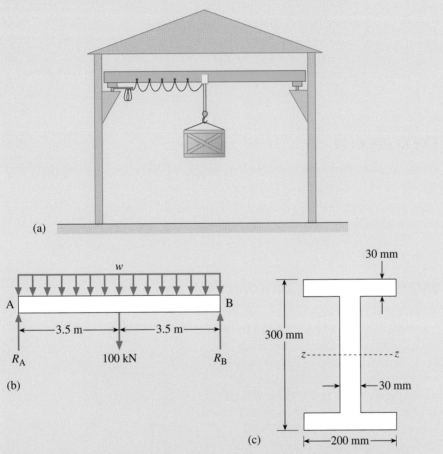

Figure 6.74   (a) Schematic of an overhead crane; (b) the loading on the crane; (c) the cross section of the I-beam

SOLUTION

The loading of the beam is shown in Figure 6.74(b). If, to start with, we ignore the beam's self-weight, the configuration is a simply supported beam with point loading at the centre. The maximum deflection, which occurs at the mid-span, can be found by the formula given in Table 6.2:

$$v_{max} = \frac{WL^3}{48EI}$$

The second moment of area of the I-beam is calculated by the formula given in Table 6.1:

$$I_z = \frac{bh^3}{12} - 2\left(\frac{cd^3}{12}\right) = \frac{0.2\ \text{m} \times (0.3\ \text{m})^3}{12} - 2 \times \frac{0.085\ \text{m} \times (0.24\ \text{m})^3}{12} = 2.54 \times 10^{-4}\ \text{m}^4$$

Putting the numerical values in the v_{max} equation gives:

$$v_{max} = \frac{100 \times 10^3\ \text{N} \times (7\ \text{m})^3}{48 \times 210 \times 10^9\ \text{Pa} \times 2.542 \times 10^{-4}\ \text{m}^4} = 13.4 \times 10^{-3}\ \text{m} = 13.4\ \text{mm}$$

EXERCISE 6.11

What would the deflection be if the self-weight of the beam were included? The density of the mild steel is 7860 kg m^{-3}.

Hint: you can just use the principle of superposition – adding the answers from the individual analyses – to find the total deflection.

SAQ 6.13 (Learning outcomes 6.3 and 6.10)

A satellite-dish installer needs to position a particular dish at a height of 3 m from the ground, to clear the neighbouring trees, for the dish to have a clear view of a satellite (Figure 6.75). The plan is to mount the dish on a pole, which will be fixed into the ground using cement. Two hollow, circular poles, made of mild steel, with outside diameters of 60 mm and 80 mm and a single wall thickness of 3 mm, are available.

Wind loading can cause forces of up to 250 N for the dish size used, but the pole deflection must be no more than 20 mm or the signal will deteriorate.

If the wind force is assumed to act at the tip of the pole at a right angle to the length of the pole, calculate the maximum deflection of the pole for the two pole diameters. Will either of the pole sizes be acceptable?

Take the elastic modulus E for the steel as 210 GPa.

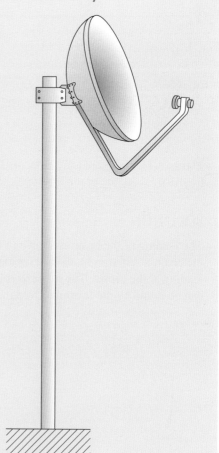

Figure 6.75 A satellite dish mounted on a pole

3 TORSION

Torsion is the engineering term used to describe a twisting moment, or torque, applied around an axis of a structural member to produce rotational deformation. Figure 6.76 shows a cylindrical bar fixed at one end, with a pair of forces applied at the other end. The forces, which are equal in magnitude but opposite in direction, form a *couple* that produces the twisting moment. The product of the forces and the distance between the forces and the longitudinal axis x of the bar gives the torque T applied to the bar:

$$T = F \times \frac{l}{2} + F \times \frac{l}{2} = Fl$$

which causes an equal but opposite reaction torque at the fixed end.

The most common examples of torsional loading are found in mechanical power transmission – for example, drive shafts and axles – and that's why any structural member designed to carry torsional loading is often called a *shaft*. However, anything that will experience a 'twisting' action during use will be experiencing torsional loading.

You are already familiar with shear stresses caused by torsion from the examples and questions in Parts 1 and 2 of Block 1. In this section, I am going to develop the relationship between stress, strain and the applied loading, just as I did for bending earlier in this part. As before, you won't have to remember the derivation, but do read through it to see how this works: see ☑ **Stress and strain relations in torsion** ☑.

Notice the difference between a 'twisting moment' and a 'bending moment': a bending moment causes rotation about the short axis (z or y) of the bar.

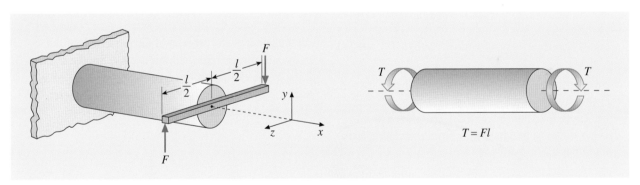

Figure 6.76   A cylindrical member subjected to a torque (pure torsion)

☑ Stress and strain relations in torsion

Figure 6.77 shows a cylindrical bar of length L, subjected to equal but opposite torques at its ends. The result is that one end of the bar has rotated *relative* to the other end by an angle θ (note that I emphasized the word relative, as this analysis would hold true even if the bar were rotating at constant angular velocity, such as is the case in shafts and axles). The angle θ is measured in radians. The line AB, previously parallel to the bar's axis, has now rotated by the angle γ, also measured in radians. You should recognize γ as the shear strain, defined as angular deformation in Part 2 of this block.

(There are 2π radians in a circle, which must be equivalent to 360°; so, to convert from degrees to radians, multiply by $2\pi/360$.)

The displacement from B to B′ in Figure 6.77 is an arc with length BB′, which subtends both the angles θ and γ. So, the arc length can be expressed in terms of both angles as:

$$L\gamma = r\theta$$

Therefore, the shear strain can be expressed as:

$$\gamma = \frac{r\theta}{L} \tag{6.21}$$

This is the strain–displacement relationship for torsion; it means that, for a given angle of twist per length θ/L, the shear strain γ produced is proportional to the distance r from the central axis of the bar.

Provided that the material is within its linear elastic region, the shear strain is associated with a shear stress τ of magnitude:

$$\tau = G\gamma \tag{6.22}$$

where G is the shear modulus. Combining this with Equation (6.21), the shear stress can be expressed as:

$$\tau = \frac{Gr\theta}{L} \tag{6.23}$$

As this equation shows, the shear stress varies over the cross section of the bar. It is zero at the centre ($r = 0$) and attains its maximum at the surface of the bar.

I will develop the relationship between the applied torque and shear stress first for a thin-walled tube. As with the analysis of a pressure vessel in Part 4, this is a useful simplification. If the radius of the tube is much greater than the thickness of its wall, we can assume that the shear stress is constant in the wall of the tube.

Figure 6.78(a) shows a section of a thin-walled tube in torsion. The magnitude of this stress must balance the applied torque T. In order to find the total force due to the shear stress, consider a small element of the tube with an area of dA, as shown in Figure 6.78(b). The shear force acting on this area is $\tau\,dA$, where dA can be taken as the product of the arc length of the segment, $r\,d\theta$, and the wall thickness t. So, the shear force in the element dA is given as $\tau r t\,d\theta$. To find the total force in the section, then, we need to integrate $d\theta$ about the circumference ($2\pi r$) of the tube:

$$T = \int_{2\pi r}^{0} \tau r t\,d\theta = \tau r t \int_{2\pi r}^{0} d\theta$$

which gives:

$$T = 2\pi r^2 t\tau \tag{6.24}$$

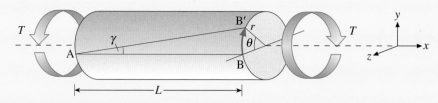

Figure 6.77   Twisting of a cylindrical member by the application of equal and opposite torques T to its ends   ▷

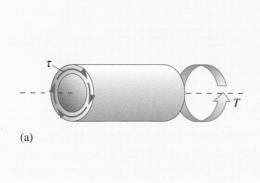

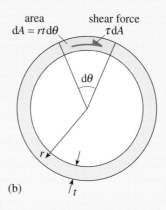

area
$dA = rt\,d\theta$

shear force
$\tau\,dA$

$d\theta$

r

t

(a)

(b)

Figure 6.78 (a) Shear stress τ in a thin-walled tube under torque T; (b) the shear force ($\tau\,dA$) acting on an element of a tube

Combining Equations (6.23) and (6.24) will give us the relation between applied torque and shear deformation:

$$T = 2\pi r^2 t \times \frac{Gr\theta}{L}$$

$$= 2\pi r^3 t \times \frac{G\theta}{L}$$

$2\pi r^3 t$ is a constant term based on the geometry of the tube. Representing this expression by the letter J and rearranging gives:

$$\frac{T}{J} = \frac{G\theta}{L} \tag{6.25}$$

Note that $J = 2\pi r^3 t$ can also be expressed as $J = 2\pi rt \times r^2 = A \times r^2$, where A is the cross-sectional area. Hence, J is another second moment of area, rather like I. However, J is measured about the longitudinal axis and is called the *polar second moment of area*, whereas I is measured about the transverse bending axis (Figure 6.79).

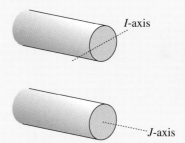

I-axis

J-axis

Figure 6.79 Where as the second moment of area that we use in bending analysis is defined about the neutral axis of a member's cross section, the polar second moment of area is defined about the member's centroidal axis

Equation (6.25) can be combined with Equation (6.23) to obtain:

$$\frac{T}{J} = \frac{\tau}{r} = \frac{G\theta}{L} \tag{6.26}$$

This equation is the torsional equivalent of the engineer's bending equation (Equation 6.7), as each term is directly analogous. For example, the twist per unit length θ/L is related to the torque T, just like the curvature $1/R$ is related to the bending moment M.

EXERCISE 6.12

(a) What are the SI units of J?

(b) Confirm that the units of each part of Equation (6.26) are equivalent.

EXERCISE 6.13

A 2 m long tube of diameter 5 mm is made of a material with maximum permissible shear strain $\gamma = 0.001$. Through what angle can the free end of the tube be twisted in torsion? (Assume that the tube is thin-walled so that you can use the equations just derived.)

Equation (6.26) applies to any radially symmetrical bar (i.e. thin- or thick-walled circular tubes and solid sections) provided that the appropriate expression for J is used. So, what is the appropriate expression for J for thick-walled tubes or solid sections?

We can imagine that a thick-walled tube, or even a solid rod, is made up of layers of thin-walled tubes, as in Figure 6.80.

When a torque is applied, the twists of these imaginary tubes must be compatible with each other. In other words, the tubes will not move relative to each other (i.e. they will not slide over each other). Hence, each thin tube has the same angular rotation, with a radial line remaining radial. Since θ is the same for each tube, the nth tube contributes a torque $T_n = J_n G\theta/L$. The total torque is therefore:

$$T = \frac{JG\theta}{L} \tag{6.27}$$

where J is the total polar moment of area. J was given earlier for a thin tube as $J = 2\pi r^3 t$. If I change the thickness t to an incremental thickness dr, then I can find J for a thick-walled tube by integrating:

$$J = \int_{r_i}^{r_o} 2\pi r^3 \, dr$$

$$= \left[\frac{1}{2}\pi r^4\right]_{r_i}^{r_o}$$

$$= \frac{1}{2}\pi\left(r_o^4 - r_i^4\right)$$

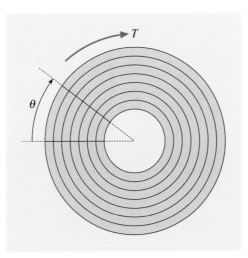

Figure 6.80   A thick-walled tube can be thought to consist of concentric thin-walled tubes, each of which goes through the same angular rotation upon application of a torque

So, the polar moment of area of a hollow circular section is given by:

$$J = \frac{1}{2}\pi\left(r_o^4 - r_i^4\right) \tag{6.28}$$

where r_i and r_o are the inner and outer radii. For a solid rod $r_i = 0$, so $J = \frac{1}{2}\pi r^4$.

If you know that $J = \frac{1}{2}\pi r^4$ for a solid shaft, it is easy to determine the formula for a hollow one: you just subtract the J of the missing piece.

EXAMPLE

A saloon car prop-shaft made of steel has outer diameter 75 mm, wall thickness 1.5 mm, length 1.5 m, and is transmitting a torque of 80 N m. Estimate the angular deflection. (Use $G = 80$ GPa for this steel.)

SOLUTION

The external and internal radii of the shaft are 37.5 mm and 36 mm respectively. The polar second moment of area for the hollow shaft, using Equation (6.28), is:

$$J = \frac{1}{2}\pi\left[\left(37.5\times10^{-3}\text{ m}\right)^4 - \left(36\times10^{-3}\text{ m}\right)^4\right] = 4.68\times10^{-7}\text{ m}^4$$

The angular deflection, given by rearranging Equation (6.27), is:

$$\theta = \frac{TL}{GJ}$$

$$= \frac{80\text{ N m}\times1.5\text{ m}}{80\times10^9\text{ Pa}\times4.68\times10^{-7}\text{ m}^4}$$

$$= 3.2\times10^{-3}\text{ rad (equivalent to }0.18°\text{)}$$

SAQ 6.14 (Learning outcome 6.11)

A tube of aluminium alloy ($G = 30$ GPa) has inner diameter 20 mm, wall thickness 2.5 mm and length 5 m.

(a) What is the J-value for this tube?

(b) If the tube is twisted by 0.4 rad, what is the torque?

(c) What is the shear strain associated with this twist?

3.1 Maximum stress from torsional loading

The other important value that we need to be able to predict for a shaft is the maximum torque that it can transmit without damage. The usual limits on this are the material capabilities: the shear yield stress τ_{yield} or shear failure stress τ_F. This will occur first in the outermost material, at the maximum radius, because that is where the shear stress is the maximum, as shown in Figure 6.81.

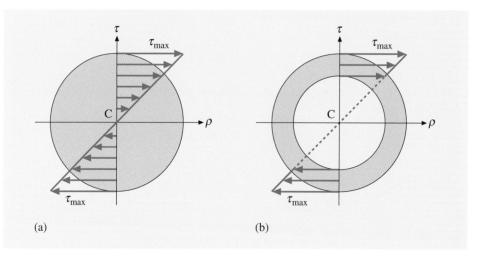

(a)   (b)

Rearranging Equation (6.26) gives:

$$\tau_{max} = \frac{Tr_{max}}{J} \tag{6.29}$$

where r_{max} is the outer radius of the shaft. Indeed, the shear stress in shafts varies linearly with the distance from the centre of the shaft, in a similar manner to bending stresses in beams. Furthermore, since the stresses in the core of a shaft are small relative to the stresses in the outer layers, a hollow shaft is more efficient in its use of stressed material than a solid one, in much the same way that material can be removed from near to the neutral axis of a beam without significantly reducing its stiffness.

EXAMPLE

The saloon car prop-shaft of the previous example was made of steel ($\tau_{yield} = 160$ MPa) with outer diameter 75 mm and wall thickness 1.5 mm.

(a) Estimate the maximum elastic torque that the shaft can be subjected to without failure by yielding.

(b) When the prop-shaft is transmitting 80 N m under normal use, what is the load factor?

SOLUTION

(a) From the earlier example, $J = 4.68 \times 10^{-7}$ m^4.

The maximum stress τ_{max} occurs at the maximum radius r_{max}. The maximum torque can be obtained by rearranging Equation (6.29) and substituting the yield stress for τ_{max}:

$$T = \frac{\tau_{max} J}{r_{max}}$$

$$= \frac{160 \times 10^6 \text{ Pa} \times 4.68 \times 10^{-7} \text{ m}^4}{37.5 \times 10^{-3} \text{ m}}$$

$$= 1997 \text{ N m}$$

(b) The load factor is the ratio of the predicted failure load to the design (or in-service) load; therefore:

load factor $= 1997/80 \approx 25$

SAQ 6.15 (Learning outcome 6.11)

The transmission shaft shown in Figure 6.82 is made up of two separate shafts joined together by welding. Shaft A is hollow with outer and inner diameters of 60 mm and 40 mm respectively, whereas shaft B is a solid section with a diameter of 50 mm. If the shaft is transmitting a 1000 N m torque, determine the maximum shear stress in the shaft.

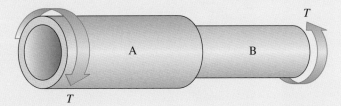

Figure 6.82   A power transmission shaft made of two segments of different diameters

SAQ 6.16 (Learning outcomes 6.11 and 6.12)

Use the torsion equation to suggest how the maximum torque that a solid circular shaft can carry will be changed by each of the following design changes. You will need to look at the polar moment of area for the shaft.

(a) Doubling its diameter.

(b) Doubling its length.

(c) Changing to a material with 50% higher yield stress.

3.2 Stress concentrations in torsion

The torsion formula $\tau = Tr/J$ can be applied to shafts having uniform, or nearly uniform, circular cross sections. If there are sudden changes in the section, such as a shoulder fillet or a keyway (Figure 6.83), then the distribution of shear stress, and shear strain, will be higher than predicted by the torsion formula. This is the same principle that you have already seen for normal and bending stresses. The determination of these stress concentrations is quite complex; so, as before, they are usually found by consulting standard tables and charts.

The maximum shear stress for a shaft containing a stress raiser (or concentrator) is found by modifying the torsion formula to include a factor K_{tr}, the *torsional stress concentration factor*:

$$\tau_{max} = K_{tr} \frac{Tr_{max}}{J} \tag{6.30}$$

Figure 6.85 gives the stress concentration factors for a shoulder fillet, a very common occurrence in power-transmitting shafts. Here, Equation (6.30) is applied to the smaller of the two connected shafts. Similar graphs for other geometries can be found in handbooks.

We have already referred to *Peterson's Stress Concentration Factors* in this course. Another useful handbook is *Roark's Formulas for Stress and Strain*, McGraw-Hill Professional Publishing.

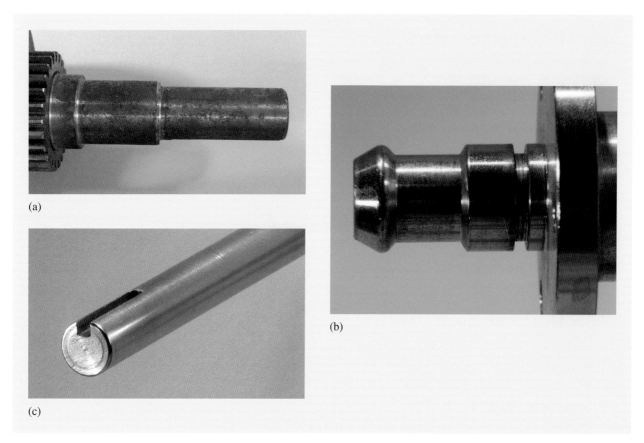

Figure 6.83   Examples of stress concentrators in shafts: (a) shoulder fillets at a change of section in an engine crank shaft; (b) a change of section in a flange coupling; (c) a keyway, which is basically a slot cut into a shaft, is used to connect shafts to other rotary members, with a fitting flat bar (key)

SAQ 6.17 (Learning outcomes 6.4 and 6.11)

The stepped shaft shown in Figure 6.84 is transmitting a torque of 1000 N m. Determine whether the maximum shear stress in the shaft exceeds 45 MPa, the allowable shear stress for the type of steel used in the design of the shaft.

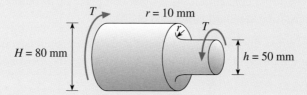

Figure 6.84   A stepped shaft

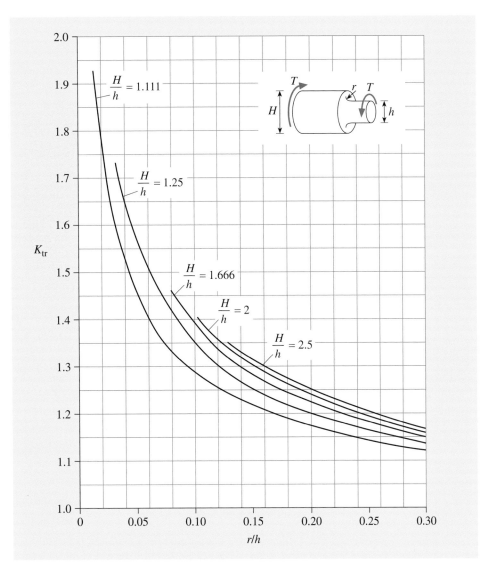

Figure 6.85 Stress concentration factors for torsion of a shaft with a shoulder fillet; adapted from Pilkey, W.D. (1997), Peterson's Stress Concentration Factors (2nd edn), Wiley & Sons, Inc, p. 166

3.3 Torsion of non-circular sections

The theory developed above for the derivation of the polar second moment of area is applicable only to circular sections, such as those commonly used for torsional members in mechanical power transmission. However, structural members with non-circular cross sections are often subjected to torsional loading in, for example, aircraft structures. The behaviour of non-circular sections under torsional loading is complex, mainly because the assumption that the cross section of the member remains plane and undistorted during torsional deformation does not hold for them. This is demonstrated schematically in Figure 6.86 for a shaft with square cross

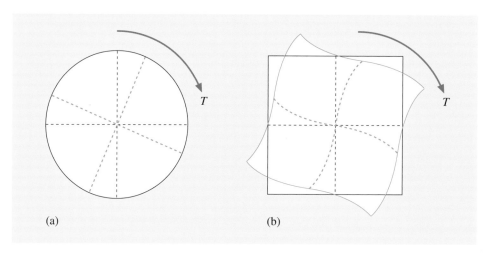

Figure 6.86 (a) When subjected to a torque, the plane section remains plane in a shaft with circular cross section; (b) the deformation in a shaft with square cross section, however, is not uniform, which causes warpage

section in comparison with one with circular cross section. When subjected to a torque, the deformation in a shaft with circular cross section occurs in such a way that the cross section remains plane, but just twists about the central axis of the shaft (Figure 6.86a). This complies with the valid assumption that both the shear stress and the shear strain vary linearly from the centre of the circular section, as shown in Figure 6.81. In shafts with non-circular sections, the stress, and hence the strain, no longer varies linearly from the centre of the shaft, owing to the loss of symmetry about the centroidal axis of the shaft, and consequently the cross sections become warped, as in the case of the square section shown in Figure 6.86(b). The greatest shear stress in square sections occurs at a point on the perimeter nearest to the centre of the square, and the shear stress at the corners reduces to zero.

The analysis of torsion in non-circular sections is quite complicated and is beyond the scope of this course. However, we can make use of J-values from handbooks for non-circular sections, which allow us to estimate the maximum shear stress and strain in these sections using Equation (6.29). Note that for non-circular sections it is no longer appropriate to refer to J as 'polar second moment of area', which is applicable to circular cross sections only. The generic term for J is *torsion constant*, which covers all sections. I have collated the torsion constants for solid and hollow circular sections, which I derived earlier, in Table 6.3, together with those for square sections that I have obtained from handbooks.

The shear stress and strain relations with applied torque for shafts with other non-circular cross sections can be found in handbooks and monographs. In general, the most efficient shafts (i.e. stiffer for a given material) are those with circular cross sections. The efficiency of the shafts with non-circular cross sections increases when the section of the shaft approaches a circle, e.g. a square section is stiffer than a rectangular section. Furthermore, the sections with tubular, closed sections (e.g. hollow square) are much stiffer than thin sections (e.g. I-beam) or open sections (Figure 6.87).

Section	Torsion constant
solid circular section	$J = \dfrac{\pi r^4}{2}$ τ_{max} is at r
hollow circular section	$J = \dfrac{\pi}{2}\left(r_o^4 - r_i^4\right)$ τ_{max} is at r_o
thin-walled circular tube	$J = 2\pi r_m^{\,3} t$ (r_m = median radius) τ_{max} is at r_m
square solid section	$J = 0.14 b^4$ τ_{max} is at $b/2$
thin-walled square tube 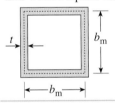	$J = b_m^{\,3} t$ (b_m = median width) τ_{max} is at $b_m/2$

Table 6.3 Torsion constants for circular and square cross sections

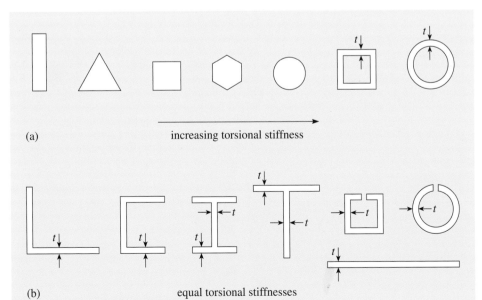

(a)   increasing torsional stiffness

(b)   equal torsional stiffnesses

Figure 6.87 Comparison of torsional stiffness of common structural members with equal cross-sectional areas: (a) sections with high, and varying, torsional stiffness; (b) sections with low, and equal, torsional stiffness

4 BUCKLING

As I mentioned at the beginning of this part, when a structural member is loaded in compression it may under some circumstances suffer an *instability* type of failure, called buckling, which is in effect runaway *bending* (Figure 6.88).

Structural components with very short lengths are resistant to bending, so in compression they exhibit no such instability (Figure 6.89). The load–deflection curves of these components are consistent with the stress–strain curve of the material under uniaxial compression. As the length of a component is increased, a condition is reached at which buckling occurs under a compressive load and the loading path departs from that of the compressive stress–strain curve of the material. This may happen when the nominal compressive stress is well below the yield stress of the material.

Buckling usually leads to failure simply because there is a limit to the amount of strain a component can tolerate under bending. It is necessary to take account of such instability during structural analysis, because it can occur at loads well below those at which conventional compressive yield failure might be expected – particularly where the deformation remains elastic. In other words, buckling instability is an important engineering failure mode in its own right.

4.1 Stability of equilibrium

Up to now I have exclusively used the term *equilibrium* to describe the condition of balanced internal and external forces. Now, I am going to use the term to help to describe the stability of structures.

Figure 6.88 Buckling instability; thermal expansions resulted in the buckling of these rails on an unusually hot summer day

(a)

(b)

(c)

Figure 6.89 The risk of buckling increases with component length: (a) stilts are less prone to buckling than (b) a pole vaulter's pole; (c) the legs (columns) of this water tower are substantially braced to prevent buckling

Consider a strut (or column) of length L being compressed by loads applied to its ends (Figure 6.90a). I will assume that this is an *ideal strut*, which means that:

1   The strut is perfectly straight and has a constant cross section.

2   The loads F are applied along an axis that passes through the centroids of the cross sections along the length of the strut.

3   The strut is made from material that is homogeneous and isotropic.

I will also assume that the ends are pin-jointed and free to rotate.

At small values of F the strut remains straight and undergoes only axial compression. To investigate the stability of such a strut we will study its behaviour when it is subjected to a small lateral disturbance.

If a very small load is applied transversely to the centre of the strut, then it will bend slightly. If the strut resumes its original straight form when the horizontal

Figure 6.90   A strut in stable equilibrium: (a) before the horizontal force is applied; (b) when the horizontal force is applied; (c) after the horizontal force is removed

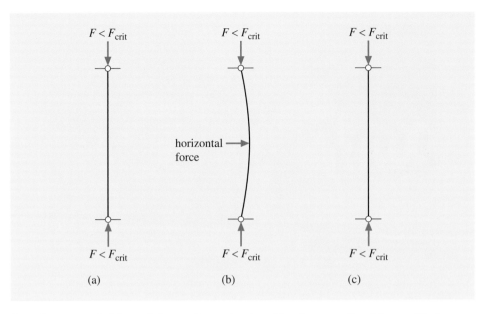

force is removed, this straight configuration is said to be one of *stable equilibrium* (Figure 6.90).

If the axial load F is increased gradually, then a critical load F_{crit} will be reached at which the strut becomes stable in its slightly bent form, and this is said to be a condition of *neutral equilibrium*. When the horizontal force is removed the strut stays in the displaced position (Figure 6.91).

If the axial load F is now increased beyond F_{crit} and the same transverse force is applied, then the displacement of the strut will become larger and larger until it collapses in bending. This condition is known as *unstable equilibrium*. But, as we are interested only in the critical condition when the applied load F reaches F_{crit}, what happens beyond this, i.e. after the strut has 'failed', does not concern us.

F_{crit}, the critical load of the system, may be defined as that load at which the straight and slightly bent configurations are equally stable. For design purposes, it is necessary to predict the value of the instability load of a member carrying a compressive load, so that the component will not buckle in service.

Figure 6.91   A strut in neutral equilibrium: (a) before the horizontal force is applied; (b) when the horizontal force is applied; (c) after the horizontal force is removed

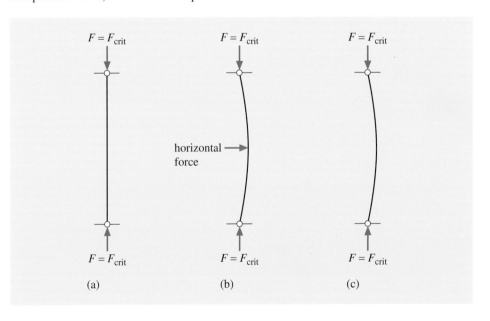

4.2 Elastic instability of a strut

I will now show you how to estimate F_{crit}. First, we must know how much freedom the ends of the strut (or column) have to deflect. I will take the case in which the ends are constrained against moving transversely, but in which they are free to rotate in any way. In practice, the strut will choose to bend about the axis for which the second moment of area of the cross section is a minimum. You can see this for yourself by compressing an ordinary ruler; it will bend and buckle in one plane preferentially (Figure 6.92).

Under the action of the small lateral disturbance, the member adopts the bent form shown in Figure 6.93(a). This is really a bending problem now. In order to find the critical load at which the strut buckles, we need to find the bending moment in the strut. To do this we will use the free-body diagram of a section of the strut shown in Figure 6.93(b). The cut face has an opposing load, equal but in opposite direction to the applied load, and a bending moment M. We can find the relation between the applied load F and the bending moment M by taking moments about the cut face at A:

$$M = Fv$$

Thus, at a distance x from the top end of the strut, the deflection (or displacement) is v and the end load F exerts a moment Fv. Now, we studied the relation between deflection v and bending moment earlier in the deflection of beams (Section 2.6); that is:

$$\frac{d^2v}{dx^2} = -\frac{M}{EI}$$

Figure 6.92   Preferential buckling direction for a ruler under compression

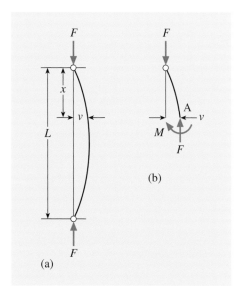

Figure 6.93   Buckling of a strut with pinned ends subjected to axial loads

Substituting for $M = Fv$ and rearranging we get:

$$\frac{d^2v}{dx^2} + \frac{Fv}{EI} = 0$$

For mathematical convenience, I will define:

$$\alpha^2 = \frac{F}{EI}$$

So, the deflection equation takes the form:

$$\frac{d^2v}{dx^2} + \alpha^2 v = 0 \qquad (6.31)$$

This is a second-order differential equation; it represents a condition that must be fulfilled by the load F and the deflections v for the strut to be in equilibrium. We seek an expression for v that will satisfy this equation. You don't need to solve differential equations as part of this course, but if you want to see how the solution works, read ▽ **Deriving the critical load for buckling** ▽.

▽ Deriving the critical load for buckling

It can be found that the following solution satisfies Equation (6.31):

$$v = A \sin \alpha x + B \cos \alpha x \qquad (6.32)$$

where A and B are constants that can be found from the boundary conditions of the strut:

at $x = 0$, $v = 0$

at $x = L$, $v = 0$.

Substituting these values into Equation (6.32) gives:

when $x = 0$, $v = 0$ and therefore $B = 0$

when $x = L$, $v = 0$ and therefore $A \sin \alpha L = 0$

The constant A is not zero – if it was there would be no deflection at all – and therefore:

$$\sin \alpha L = 0$$

This occurs when $\alpha L = 0$, π, 2π, 3π, etc., or in other words when:

$$\alpha L = n\pi \qquad (6.33)$$

Note that $\alpha L = 0$ is a trivial solution. It refers to the case where $\alpha = 0$; the strut is not loaded ($F = 0$).

Combining Equations (6.31) and (6.33) and substituting for $\alpha^2 = F/EI$ gives:

$$F = \frac{n^2\pi^2 EI}{L^2}$$

The smallest value of F_{crit} at which buckling can occur is obtained when $n = 1$, and this is known as the *Euler load*:

$$F_{crit} = \frac{\pi^2 EI}{L^2}$$

Larger values of n represent buckling into more complicated shapes, and we will not be concerned with them here. They occur at higher loads, if at all.

△

The critical load is found to be:

$$F_{\text{crit}} = \frac{\pi^2 EI}{L^2} \qquad (6.34)$$

This is known as the *Euler formula* after Leonard Euler (pronounced 'oiler'), the Swiss mathematician (Figure 6.94). The product *EI*, you may recall, is known as *flexural rigidity* and it is a measure of the strut's stiffness in bending.

Figure 6.94   Leonard Euler (1707–1783)

EXAMPLE

A metal bar of circular cross section has length 5 m and diameter 20 mm ($E = 200$ GPa, $\sigma_{\text{yield}} = 200$ MPa). Estimate:

(a) the material yield load

(b) the buckling load.

How do they compare?

SOLUTION

(a) The yield load estimate is:

$$F = \sigma_{\text{yield}} A = 63 \text{ kN}$$

(b) The buckling load estimate can be determined by substituting for $I = \pi r^4/4$ in the Euler formula (Equation 6.34):

$$F = \frac{\pi^2 EI}{L^2} = \frac{\pi^2 E \pi r^4}{4L^2}$$

$$= \frac{\pi^3 \times 200 \times 10^9 \text{ Pa} \times \left(10 \times 10^{-3} \text{ m}\right)^4}{4 \times \left(5 \text{ m}\right)^2}$$

$$= 620 \text{ N}$$

which is only 1% of the yield load!

EXERCISE 6.14

(a) If the diameter of the metal bar in the previous example is increased to 63.5 mm, what is the buckling load?

(b) What is the increase in the mass of the bar?

SAQ 6.18 (Learning outcomes 6.3 and 6.14–6.16)

The control linkage of an aircraft elevator includes an aluminium alloy rod ($E = 70$ GPa) of length 2.4 m and solid circular cross section 20 mm in diameter, required to transmit a compressive force of 400 N.

(a) What is the buckling load?

(b) What is the safety factor?

(c) Estimate the minimum (or critical) diameter of solid rod able to to withstand buckling for the same 400 N load.

This weakness of members in compression due to buckling is an expensive problem, requiring the use of a lot of extra material. What can we do to improve the resistance to buckling without using so much material? From the Euler formula, $F = \pi^2 EI/L^2$, you can see that we must increase E, increase I or decrease L. Increasing E is rarely a practical solution. The materials are usually predetermined by other factors. It might be possible to change from, say, aluminium to steel, but the aluminium was probably being used for lightness, so the denser steel will not be welcome. Reducing the overall length L may not be practical, as it would probably mean redesigning the whole structure.

Increasing the second moment of area I looks an interesting possibility. To do this means moving the material further away from the bending axis to make it more effective in resisting bending. The material can be spread out by making a hollow section, e.g. a circular tube. To see how this works, do Exercise 6.15.

EXERCISE 6.15

The solid 20 mm diameter, 5 m long rod of the last example is to be replaced by a tube with 52 mm average diameter and 2 mm wall thickness.

(a) By what proportions are the cross-sectional area and mass changed?

(b) Estimate the new buckling load.

(c) By what factor has this changed?

You can find formulas for the calculation of the second moments of area of the sections in Table 6.1.

The hollow tube gives a considerable improvement in the critical buckling load, although it is often still far from the material yield stress limit. The modern lamp-post shows that the hollow tube can be a good way to achieve better I values and bending resistance (Figure 6.95). Other sections that one sees commonly are the I-section, angle,

Figure 6.95 A typical steel-tube lamp-post

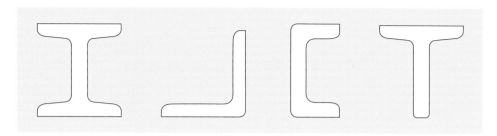

channel and T-section (Figure 6.96). These are cheaper to produce than the hollow tube, but they still retain the advantage of better I values than round or square solid sections. However, as you discovered with the buckling of a plastic ruler (Figure 6.92), where sections have different I values about their principal axes (such as rectangles and I-sections), the buckling will occur about the axis that has the smallest I value (i.e. less resistance to bending), provided that the ends of the strut are not constrained.

4.3 Buckling of struts with other support conditions

To cover cases where the end conditions are other than those assumed in the analysis I have just shown, a factor K is introduced into the Euler equation, giving the general expression:

$$F_{\text{crit}} = \frac{K\pi^2 EI}{L^2} \tag{6.35}$$

where K is a constant for a given set of end restraints. Example cases are shown in Figure 6.97. $K = 1$ for the case I just analysed and $K = 4$ for the case where the ends are allowed no transverse deflection and no rotation.

The boundary conditions associated with $K = 1$ can be achieved only by having a frictionless ball joint, so they are clearly ideal rather than practical. A *pin joint* or hinge is considered to be the nearest approach to the ideal frictionless ball joint that can be made in practical situations; the cylindrical nature of the 'pin' restricts rotation at the end to one plane only. Similarly, it is difficult, in practice, to achieve the highly constrained boundary conditions associated with $K = 4$.

Choosing the appropriate value for K may not be so straightforward when the buckling characteristics of a compression member within a structure are required. For example, look at Figure 6.98, which shows a truss structure buckling under the application of compressive loads. Although the truss in the figure may be assumed to be pin-jointed for the purpose of an analysis, in practice it is likely to be assembled with fixed or partially fixed joints. The ends of a compression member in this truss cannot rotate without bending all the other members at the end joints. Determining the degree of end fixation of such a compression member is largely a matter of educated guesswork, since the element may buckle in any direction and is restrained by the torsional and bending stiffnesses of adjacent members. So, if a member is restrained by stiffer members next to it, then the joints of the member would be classified as *clamped*, as in Figure 6.97(d); consequently K would be high (up to 4). However, if the neighbouring members are more flexible, then the joints would

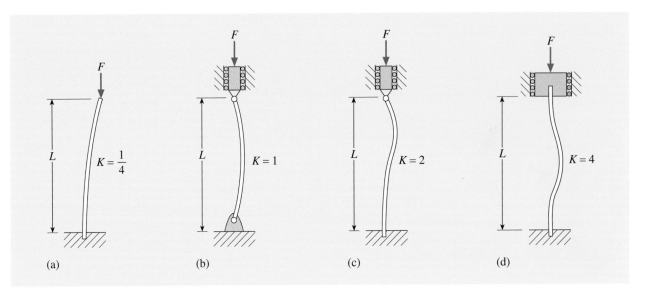

Figure 6.97   Restraint constant K for various end conditions of struts: (a) clamped (fixed) end–free end, (b) hinged–hinged, (c) clamped–hinged and (d) clamped–clamped

Figure 6.98   Buckling of a truss structure

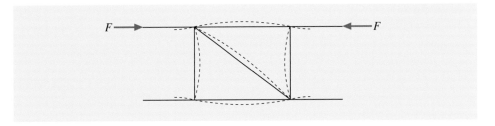

have relatively less constraint, so that K would be smaller. Although this type of guesswork may provide a preliminary estimate of the buckling characteristics of the structural members, a more accurate analysis requires more advanced techniques, such as the stiffness matrix method that I introduced in Part 5 of this block.

EXAMPLE

A student climbs up a 16 m tall flagpole to place a mascot on its top. The student's mass is about 90 kg; the pole, which is made of an aluminium alloy, has an outside diameter of 100 mm and has 6 mm wall thickness. Can he get to the top before the pole buckles? Neglect the weight of the pole itself and assume that he manages to keep his centre of gravity close to the pole axis. ($E = 70$ GPa.)

SOLUTION

We want to know whether the critical buckling load, given by Equation (6.34), is exceeded when the student reaches the top, i.e. $L = 16$ m. The second moment of area of the hollow pole can be calculated by the formula given in Table 6.1:

$$I = \frac{\pi(r_o^4 - r_i^4)}{4} = \frac{\pi\left[(50 \times 10^{-3} \text{ m})^4 - (44 \times 10^{-3} \text{ m})^4\right]}{4} = 1.965 \times 10^{-6} \text{ m}^4$$

The flagpole is fixed at the bottom, but the flag end is free as in the case of Figure 6.97(a); so the restraint constant K is 1/4. The critical buckling load is then:

$$F_{\text{crit}} = \frac{K\pi^2 EI}{L^2} = \frac{(1/4)\times\pi^2 \times 70\times 10^9 \text{ Pa}\times 1.965\times 10^{-6} \text{ m}^4}{(16\text{ m})^2} = 1325 \text{ N}$$

which corresponds to a mass of 135 kg. This is higher than the student's mass of 90 kg, so he might just make it! However, considering the lack of a safety factor (and the fact that we have neglected the self-weight of the pole), it would be inadvisable to try.

SAQ 6.19 (Learning outcomeS 6.14 and 6.15)

A 100 mm wide rectangular wood plank is used for a 7 m column with one end fixed and one end hinged, as in Figure 6.97(c). It must support an axial load of 5 kN.

What is the minimum thickness for the plank if a load factor of 5 is used? The modulus of the wood is 10 GPa.

Hint: the thickness affects the second moment of area I of the section.

4.4 Failure stress for struts

For design purposes, it is often preferred to express the critical buckling load in terms of stress, as this can be compared with other critical stresses for the material, in particular the yield stress in compression. The critical buckling stress can simply be obtained by dividing the critical buckling load by the cross-sectional area of the strut:

$$\sigma_{\text{crit}} = \frac{F_{\text{crit}}}{A} = \frac{K\pi^2 EI}{AL^2} \qquad (6.36)$$

This equation can be put into a more useful form if we define the second moment of area I as:

$$I = Ar^2$$

where A is the area of the cross section and r is called the *radius of gyration* (which has units of length). The radius of gyration is defined in the same axis as the second moment of area, for example:

$$r_z = \sqrt{\frac{I_z}{A}} \quad \text{and} \quad r_y = \sqrt{\frac{I_y}{A}} \qquad (6.37)$$

The radius of gyration can be used to identify the direction of buckling; a strut will buckle, if it is not restrained, in a direction with the *smallest radius of gyration*. Using the plastic ruler example again, the radius of gyration for the ruler is much smaller in the direction of its thickness than in the direction of its width.

Substituting for $r^2 = I/A$ into Equation (6.36) and rearranging, we get the critical stress for buckling as:

$$\sigma_{\text{crit}} = \frac{K\pi^2 E}{(L/r)^2} \qquad (6.38)$$

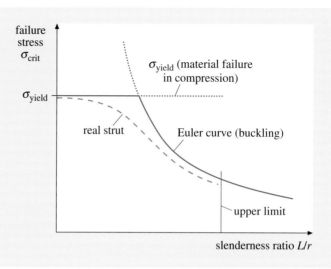

Figure 6.99   Failure stress as a function of the slenderness ratio of a strut

Since r is of the same order as the width of the strut, the ratio L/r, which is known as the *slenderness ratio* of the strut, gives some indication of the physical form or aspect ratio of the strut. This is an important concept, since L/r is the only geometric parameter in Equation (6.38) that has an effect on the stress at which the buckling occurs. Thus, for given values of restraint factor K and elastic modulus E, it is possible to calculate the failure stress for a practical strut having a given slenderness (or aspect) ratio L/r (Figure 6.99).

I have plotted σ_{crit} versus L/r described by Equation (6.36) in Figure 6.99 as the 'Euler' curve. Note that the critical stress calculated by Equation (6.38) exceeds the compressive yield stress of the material at low L/r ratios. Obviously, this means that at low L/r ratios the strut will start yielding in compression and, therefore, that the Euler equation, which is based on the assumption that the material must behave elastically, will no longer apply.

EXAMPLE

For an aluminium alloy the proof stress in compression is 200 MPa and the elastic modulus E is 70 GPa. What is the critical slenderness ratio for a strut hinged at both ends (i.e. $K = 1$) to just fail by buckling?

SOLUTION

Assuming ideal strut behaviour, the critical slenderness ratio is found by taking the compressive proof stress of the alloy as the critical buckling stress. Rearranging Equation (6.38) gives:

$$\frac{L}{r} = \left(\frac{K\pi^2 E}{\sigma_{crit}} \right)^{1/2} = \left(\frac{1 \times \pi^2 \times 70 \times 10^9 \text{ Pa}}{200 \times 10^6 \text{ Pa}} \right)^{1/2} = 59$$

EXERCISE 6.16

What would be the critical slenderness ratio if the strut in the above example were made of steel, which has a yield strength of 300 MPa and an elastic modulus of 210 GPa?

When L/r is large, there is a marked tendency for buckling to occur at very low stresses. Thus, there exists an effective upper limit of L/r (shown by the vertical line in Figure 6.99) beyond which compression members have little load-bearing ability and can be neglected.

Now, I must remind you that the theories I have presented to you above assume that the struts do not show any lateral deflection until the load reaches the critical value, as shown in Figure 6.100. A *real* strut generally violates one or more of the initial assumptions upon which they are based; for example, the strut may have some initial curvature or the loading upon it may not be precisely central. A real strut usually starts to bend almost immediately after any load is applied, and the deflection curve for a real strut may never reach the critical buckling load for ideal struts, as shown in Figure 6.100. Instead, the strut fails by yielding at some point, and afterwards the load-carrying capacity of the strut shows a decrease as the central deflection of the strut increases.

Looking back at Figure 6.99, you can see that the failure stress of a real strut is lower than predicted by the ideal strut case. So, using the ideal strut calculations can lead to overestimation of the failure stresses in real struts. Fortunately, it is possible to include the initial imperfections of the struts in the mathematical analysis, which gives a much more accurate prediction of the failure stresses. However, the derivation and the application of these methods are rather complex; therefore, they are not covered in this course. The accuracy of the ideal strut case is sufficient for our purposes, especially when used with a suitable safety factor.

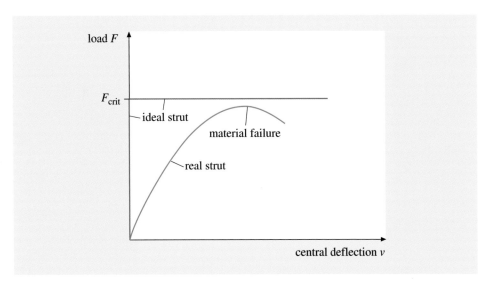

Figure 6.100   Observed and theoretical load–deflection curves for a strut during buckling

EXAMPLE

Calculate the failure load of a high-strength steel strut of length 0.5 m, of hollow rectangular section 50 mm wide by 25 mm deep, having a constant wall thickness of 2 mm.

Assume that the modulus of elasticity E is 200 GPa, that the yield stress of steel is 1000 MPa and that the restraint factor K is 1.0. Regard either yielding or buckling as failure.

SOLUTION

We need to determine whether the critical buckling stress exceeds the compressive yield stress of the material. The section of the strut is shown in Figure 6.101.

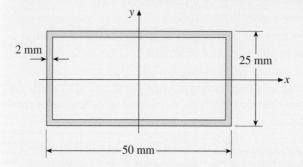

Figure 6.101   Cross section of a hollow rectangular strut

The critical buckling stress is given by Equation (6.38):

$$\sigma_{crit} = \frac{K\pi^2 E}{\left(L/r\right)^2}$$

The only parameter on the right-hand side of the equation that we need to determine is the radius of gyration for the section. The second moment of inertia for a hollow rectangular section is found by the formula given in Table 6.1:

$$I = \frac{bh^3}{12} - \frac{b_i h_i^3}{12}$$

We know that the strut will buckle about the axis about which the second moment of area is the least. Therefore, we need to compare the I values about the x- and y-axes:

$$I_x = \frac{50\times10^{-3} \text{ m}\times\left(25\times10^{-3} \text{ m}\right)^3}{12} - \frac{46\times10^{-3} \text{ m}\times\left(21\times10^{-3} \text{ m}\right)^3}{12}$$
$$= 2.96\times10^{-8} \text{ m}^4$$

Similarly:

$$I_y = \frac{25 \times 10^{-3} \text{ m} \times \left(50 \times 10^{-3} \text{ m}\right)^3}{12} - \frac{21 \times 10^{-3} \text{ m} \times \left(46 \times 10^{-3} \text{ m}\right)^3}{12}$$
$$= 9.01 \times 10^{-8} \text{ m}^4$$

Since $I_x < I_y$, the strut will bend preferentially about the x-axis. The cross-sectional area of the strut is:

$$A = \left(50 \times 10^{-3} \text{ m} \times 25 \times 10^{-3} \text{ m}\right) - \left(46 \times 10^{-3} \text{ m} \times 21 \times 10^{-3} \text{ m}\right) = 2.84 \times 10^{-4} \text{ m}^2$$

The radius of gyration about the x-axis calculated by Equation (6.36) is:

$$r_x = \sqrt{\frac{I_x}{A}} = \sqrt{\frac{2.96 \times 10^{-8} \text{ m}^4}{2.84 \times 10^{-4} \text{ m}^2}} = 10.21 \times 10^{-3} \text{ m}$$

Now we can calculate the critical buckling stress:

$$\sigma_{\text{crit}} = \frac{K\pi^2 E}{\left(L/r\right)^2} = \frac{1 \times \pi^2 \times 200 \times 10^9}{\left(0.5/0.01021\right)^2} = 823 \times 10^6 \text{ Pa} = 823 \text{ MPa}$$

This is less than the compressive proof stress of the material (1000 MPa), so the strut will fail by buckling. The buckling load is:

$$F_{\text{crit}} = \sigma_{\text{crit}} \times A = 823 \times 10^6 \text{ Pa} \times 2.84 \times 10^{-7} \text{ m}^2 = 233\,732 \text{ N} \approx 234 \text{ kN}$$

SAQ 6.20 (Learning outcomes 6.14 and 6.16)

If the strut in the previous example (Figure 6.101) is constrained at the ends so that it cannot buckle in the plane of the smaller side, recalculate the failure load.

5 SUMMARY

This part of Block 1 has covered three important methods of loading and failure, and given you the tools to analyse them when they occur.

One of the things that you have probably realized while studying this part is how the answers to the analysis of what at first sight is a relatively simple problem (like the bending of a beam) can actually be greatly complicated by just how the beam is supported, and what assumptions are made if this isn't known precisely. I have already indicated that many structural problems, such as those introduced in this section, are now routinely modelled and solved by computer packages rather than by longhand calculation; but that doesn't change the fact that the assumptions of loading and support affect the results no matter what method is used to perform the calculations. Understanding the problem thoroughly in the first place is just as important as using appropriate, accurate methods to find a solution.

We are coming to the end of this block, the overall aim of which has been to teach you the fundamentals of stress analysis in materials, components and structures. In the final part you will be exposed to some of the complexities surrounding stress analysis in practice, before we move on to a more detailed look at what causes failure in the second block of the course.

LEARNING OUTCOMES

After studying this part you should be able to do the following:

6.1 Determine the magnitude and distribution of longitudinal stresses and strains in beams subjected to bending moments.

6.2 Describe how the cross-sectional areas and shapes influence the stiffness and strength of structural members subjected to bending moments.

6.3 Calculate second moments of area of sections of common structural members.

6.4 Recognize, and calculate, the effect of stress concentrations on the performance of beams and shafts.

6.5 Identify whether a beam is statically determinate.

6.6 Model and calculate the support loads for structural members.

6.7 Calculate and plot the distributions of bending moment and shear force within structural members that are subjected to transverse loads.

6.8 Estimate the maximum shear stress in beams with simple sections.

6.9 Calculate the combined effect of bending moment and axial loading on the stresses in beams.

6.10 Calculate the maximum deflection of beams subjected to bending moments.

6.11 Calculate the magnitude and distribution of shear stresses and strains in circular shafts subjected to torsional loading.

6.12 Select suitable circular shafts to carry given torsional loads.

6.13 Recognize the efficiency of cross-sectional shape of the shafts in terms of torsional strength and stiffness.

6.14 Determine the buckling loads of perfect (idealized) struts subjected to compressive loads under various end conditions.

6.15 Select suitable compressive members to resist buckling under given loading.

6.16 Assess the loading of components and structures to determine the possibility of failure by bending, torsion or buckling.

ANSWERS TO EXERCISES

EXERCISE 6.1

The curved beam is designed to reduce the tensile stresses in the beam. You should recall from Part 5 that *arches* are used in masonry bridges and structures to eliminate tensile forces. The design of the Skye Bridge is not a complete arch, i.e. not all the tensile forces are eliminated; but they are significantly reduced to allow a longer span length to be designed.

EXERCISE 6.2

The minimum radius the wire can sustain (substituting the yield stress for σ_x) is:

$$R = \frac{E(d/2)}{\sigma_x} = \frac{50 \times 10^9 \text{ Pa} \times \left(1 \times 10^{-3} \text{ m}/2\right)}{40 \times 10^6 \text{ Pa}} = 0.625 \text{ m}$$

This is larger than the reel used, so the wire will have yielded when being wound on to the reel.

EXERCISE 6.3

When it is bent across its width (Figure 6.24a), the second moment of area of the ruler is:

$$I = \frac{bh^3}{12} = \frac{3.5 \times 10^{-3} \text{ m} \times \left(38 \times 10^{-3} \text{ m}\right)^3}{12} = 1.6 \times 10^{-8} \text{ m}^4$$

When it is bent across its thickness (Figure 6.24b), the height h of the section becomes the shorter dimension of the ruler; so, the second moment of area of the ruler becomes:

$$I = \frac{bh^3}{12} = \frac{38 \times 10^{-3} \text{ m} \times \left(3.5 \times 10^{-3} \text{ m}\right)^3}{12} = 0.0136 \times 10^{-8} \text{ m}^4$$

So, the former case is $1.6/0.0136 \approx 118$ times stiffer in bending.

EXERCISE 6.4

The second moment of area of the built-up section is the I of the square section minus the I of the circle of radius r $(d/2)$:

$$I = \frac{bb^3}{12} - \frac{\pi r^4}{4}$$
$$= \frac{b^4}{12} - \frac{\pi r^4}{4}$$

EXERCISE 6.5

By rearranging the engineer's bending equation, to relate stress to bending moment and the beam geometry, we obtain:

$$\sigma = \frac{My}{I}$$

where

$$
\begin{aligned}
I &= \frac{b^4}{12} - \frac{\pi r^4}{4} \\
&= \frac{\left(50 \times 10^{-3}\ \text{m}\right)^4}{12} - \frac{\pi \left(17.5 \times 10^{-3}\ \text{m}\right)^4}{4} \\
&= 4.47 \times 10^{-7}\ \text{m}
\end{aligned}
$$

At the surface $y = 25 \times 10^{-3}$ m, thus:

$$\sigma = \frac{2 \times 10^3\ \text{N m} \times 25 \times 10^{-3}\ \text{m}}{4.47 \times 10^{-7}\ \text{m}^4} = 112\ \text{MPa}$$

EXERCISE 6.6

We will need to employ Equation (6.8) and the relevant chart of stress concentration factors for our geometry (Figure 6.29a) to calculate the stress in the gear tooth. Extrapolating between the curves $h/H = 2$ and $h/H = 3$ in Figure 6.29(a) for $h/H = 2.5$ at $r/h = 0.25$, we find that the stress concentration factor K_b for our geometry is approximately 1.4.

The second moment of area of the smaller cross section of the beam is calculated from the rectangular-section formula (Table 6.1):

$$
\begin{aligned}
I_z &= \frac{bh^3}{12} \\
&= \frac{12 \times 10^{-3}\ \text{m} \times \left(20 \times 10^{-3}\ \text{m}\right)^3}{12} \\
&= 8.0 \times 10^{-9}\ \text{m}^4
\end{aligned}
$$

The maximum stress occurs at $y = h/2$, near the fillet. Substituting all the numerical values into Equation (6.8) gives:

$$
\begin{aligned}
\sigma_{\text{max}} &= K_b \frac{M_{\text{max}}\, y}{I} \\
&= 1.4 \times \frac{100\ \text{N m} \times 10 \times 10^{-3}\ \text{m}}{8.0 \times 10^{-9}\,\text{m}^4} \\
&= 175\ \text{MPa}
\end{aligned}
$$

This value can be used as an initial estimate for the maximum stress in the root of the gear tooth.

EXERCISE 6.7

(a) The free-body diagram of the beam is given in Figure 6.102(a), where I put a vertical reaction at the roller support and a vertical and a horizontal reaction at the knife-edge support. I have shown the UDL as a series of small arrows, linked together so that they are not confused with point forces.

(b) There are three unknowns: R_{Ay}, R_{Bx} and R_{By}. As we have three equilibrium equations ($\sum F_x = 0$, $\sum F_y = 0$ and $\sum M = 0$), the beam is statically determinate.

(c) First, there is only one horizontal force on the diagram: the reaction force at B, R_{Bx}. As the system is in equilibrium, and there is nothing opposing this force, then it must be equal to zero. In practice, for problems where all the applied loads are perpendicular to the beam, the horizontal reaction forces can be ignored.

For convenience, when finding the two vertical reactions, I converted the UDL to the equivalent point force wl, as shown in Figure 6.102(b). I then used moment equilibrium about one of the supports so that the reaction force at that support would not appear in the equation. So, taking moments about, say, support A (remembering that anticlockwise rotations have positive moments) gives:

$$\sum M_A = 0$$

$$-\left(wl \times \frac{l}{2}\right) - W(L - l) + R_{By}L = 0$$

Rearranging gives:

$$R_{By} = \frac{wl^2/2 + W(L - l)}{L}$$

$$= \frac{5\ \text{kN m}^{-1} \times (4\ \text{m})^2/2 + [20\ \text{kN} \times (10\ \text{m} - 4\ \text{m})]}{10\ \text{m}}$$

$$= 16\ \text{kN}$$

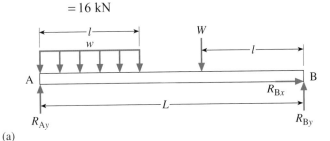

(a)

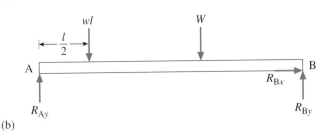

(b)

Figure 6.102   (a) Free-body diagram of a simply supported beam with a UDL and a point load; (b) substitution of the UDL with an equivalent point load

By using the equilibrium in the y-direction, I can now find the other vertical reaction:

$$\sum F_y = 0$$
$$-wl - W + R_{Ay} + R_{By} = 0$$

Thus:

$$R_{Ay} = 5 \text{ kN m}^{-1} \times 4 \text{ m} + 20 \text{ kN} - 16 \text{ kN} = 24 \text{ kN}$$

EXERCISE 6.8

(a) As there are two unknowns (i.e. M_A and R_{Ay}) and two equilibrium equations ($\sum F_y = 0$ and $\sum M_A = 0$, not counting the horizontal reaction), the beam is statically determinate.

(b) You can calculate the weight of the beam by multiplying its volume by its density and the acceleration due to gravity g:

$$\text{weight of the beam} = A \times L \times g \times \text{density}$$
$$= 0.4 \text{ m} \times 0.1 \text{ m} \times 3 \text{ m} \times 9.81 \text{ m s}^{-2} \times 400 \text{ kg m}^{-3}$$
$$= 471 \text{ m kg s}^{-2}$$
$$= 471 \text{ N}$$

This can be expressed as a UDL (or load intensity along the beam) by dividing the total weight by the length of the beam, which gives $w = 157 \text{ N m}^{-1}$.

(c) Applying equilibrium in the y-direction gives:

$$R_{Ay} = wL + W$$
$$= 157 \text{ N m}^{-1} \times 3 \text{ m} + 700 \text{ N}$$
$$= 1171 \text{ N}$$

The moment reaction M_A at the support is found by applying the moment equilibrium about the built-in support A. Taking anticlockwise moments as positive:

$$\sum M_A = 0$$
$$-w \times L \times (L/2) - W \times L - M_A = 0$$

Therefore:

$$M_A = -(157 \text{ N m}^{-1} \times 3 \text{ m} \times 1.5 \text{ m}) + -(700 \text{ N} \times 3 \text{ m})$$
$$= -2807 \text{ N m}$$

EXERCISE 6.9

(a) The larger the bending moment is, the higher the risk of beam fracture will be; so, we would like to reduce the bending moment. The bending-moment diagram of the simply supported beam with an off-centre point load as shown in Figure 6.43 gives the magnitude of the peak bending moment as:

$$M = \frac{Wab}{L}$$

The maximum bending moment occurs for a configuration where the point load is applied at the midpoint of the beam, where $a = b = L/2$. This gives the maximum bending moment as $WL/4$.

The minimum bending moment occurs when the point load is applied at either support, where it will be zero. So, placing the vase just over one of the supports seems to be a good idea, if the strength of the shelf (*the beam*) is suspect.

(b) Placing the vase on a support doubles the load on that particular support and increases the risk of fixing failure. It would be better, to avoid support failure, to put the vase in the midpoint of the shelf where the load is shared by the two supports.

The decision is yours!

EXERCISE 6.10

The problem is obviously a cantilever subjected to a point load at the free end plus a continuous UDL. Figure 6.58 presents solutions to each case separately; that is, a cantilever with a point load at the free end, and a cantilever with a UDL. We can, therefore, use the principle of superposition to find a solution to our configurations by simply summing the solutions given in Figure 6.58. The vertical reaction at the free end is equal to the sum of the shear forces:

$$\begin{aligned}
R_y &= W + wL \\
&= 750 \text{ N} + (160 \text{ N m} \times 3 \text{ m}) \\
&= 1230 \text{ N}
\end{aligned}$$

Since there is no horizontal load component applied to the board, the horizontal reaction force at the built-in end is zero. The bending-moment reaction at the built-in end is also the sum of both cases in Figure 6.58:

$$\begin{aligned}
M &= -WL - \frac{wL^2}{2} \\
&= -(750 \text{ N} \times 3 \text{ m}) - \frac{160 \text{ N m}^{-1} \times (3 \text{ m})^2}{2} \\
&= -2970 \text{ N m}
\end{aligned}$$

This is also the maximum bending moment, which always occurs at the built-in end of the cantilevers.

EXERCISE 6.11

The maximum deflection due to both the weight of the crane W and the self-weight of the beam can be obtained by determining the deflection for each case and adding them (i.e. the method of superposition).

The weight of the beam can be expressed as a distributed load w, as shown in Figure 6.74, by dividing the whole weight of the beam by its length:

$$
\begin{aligned}
w &= \frac{\text{weight}}{\text{length}} \\
&= \frac{\text{volume} \times \text{density} \times g}{\text{length}} \\
&= \frac{\left[2 \times (0.2 \text{ m} \times 0.03 \text{ m}) + (0.24 \text{ m} \times 0.03 \text{ m})\right] \times 7 \text{ m} \times 7860 \text{ kg m}^{-3} \times 9.81 \text{ m s}^{-2}}{7 \text{ m}} \\
&= 1480 \text{ N m}^{-1}
\end{aligned}
$$

The maximum deflection due to the self-weight of the beam is then obtained using the formula in Table 6.2 for a simply supported beam subjected to distributed load:

$$
\begin{aligned}
v_{\max} &= \frac{5wL^4}{384EI} \\
&= \frac{5 \times 1480 \text{ N m}^{-1} \times (7 \text{ m})^4}{384 \times 210 \times 10^9 \text{ Pa} \times 2.542 \times 10^{-4} \text{ m}^4} \\
&= 0.87 \times 10^{-3} \text{ m} \\
&= 0.87 \text{ mm}
\end{aligned}
$$

The total deflection will then be 13.4 mm + 0.87 mm = 14.3 mm.

EXERCISE 6.12

(a) The units of J are $\text{m}^2 \times \text{m}^2 = \text{m}^4$, which are the same units as I.

(b) T/J has units of $\text{N m m}^{-4} = \text{N m}^{-3}$

τ/r has units of $\text{N m}^{-2} \text{ m}^{-1} = \text{N m}^{-3}$

$G\theta/L$ has units of $\text{N m}^{-2} \text{ m}^{-1} = \text{N m}^{-3}$

The three parts of the equation, therefore, all have the same units.

EXERCISE 6.13

The tube radius $r = 0.0025$ m.

Assuming a thin-walled tube, rearranging Equation (6.21) gives:

$$
\theta = \frac{\gamma L}{r} = \frac{0.001 \times 2 \text{ m}}{0.0025 \text{ m}} = 0.8 \text{ rad, or } 45.8°
$$

EXERCISE 6.14

(a) $r = 31.75 \text{ mm} = 31.75 \times 10^{-3} \text{ m}$

$$I = \frac{1}{4}\pi r^4 = \frac{\pi(31.75 \times 10^{-3} \text{ m})^4}{4} = 8.0 \times 10^{-7} \text{ m}^4$$

$$F_{\text{crit}} = \frac{\pi^2 EI}{L^2} = \frac{\pi^2 \times 200 \times 10^9 \times 8.0 \times 10^{-7} \text{ m}^4}{(5 \text{ m})^2} = 63 \text{ kN}$$

This strut achieves a load equal to the material yield load of the earlier one.

(b) Its diameter is increased by $63.5 \text{ mm}/20 \text{ mm} = 3.175$ times.

The mass of material, which is proportional for r^2, increased by a factor of $(3.175)^2 \approx 10$.

EXERCISE 6.15

(a) The original solid bar has the cross-sectional area:

$$A_{\text{solid}} = \pi r^2 = \pi(10 \times 10^{-3} \text{ m})^2 = 3.14 \times 10^{-4} \text{ m}^2$$

The new circular tube has an external diameter of 52 mm and an internal diameter of 48 mm. Its cross-sectional area is:

$$A_{\text{tube}} = \pi(r_o^2 - r_i^2) = \pi\left[(26 \times 10^{-3} \text{ m})^2 - (24 \times 10^{-3} \text{ m})^2\right] = 3.14 \times 10^{-4} \text{ m}^2$$

So, the cross-sectional area of the tube (and hence its mass) is the same as that of the solid bar.

(b) The second moment of area of the hollow circular tube is:

$$I = \frac{\pi(r_o^4 - r_i^4)}{4} = \frac{\pi\left[(26 \times 10^{-3} \text{ m})^4 - (24 \times 10^{-3} \text{ m})^4\right]}{4} = 9.83 \times 10^{-8} \text{ m}^4$$

The critical load is:

$$F_{\text{crit}} = \frac{\pi^2 EI}{L^2} = \frac{\pi^2(200 \times 10^9 \text{ Pa} \times 9.83 \times 10^{-8} \text{ m}^4)}{(5 \text{ m})^2} = 7760 \text{ N}$$

(c) The improvement in the buckling resistance of using a hollow tube of the same mass as the solid bar is $7760/620 = 12.5$ times.

EXERCISE 6.16

Rearranging Equation (6.38):

$$\frac{L}{r} = \left(\frac{K\pi^2 E}{\sigma_{\text{crit}}}\right)^{1/2} = \left(\frac{1 \times \pi^2 \times 210 \times 10^9}{300 \times 10^6}\right)^{1/2} = 83$$

ANSWERS TO SELF-ASSESSMENT QUESTIONS

SAQ 6.1

(a) For the solid beam:

$$I = \frac{b^4}{12} = 5.21 \times 10^{-7} \text{ m}^4$$

(b) With the centre removed:

$$I = \frac{b^4}{12} - \frac{\pi r^4}{4}$$

$$= 5.21 \times 10^{-7} \text{ m}^4 - \frac{\pi (15 \times 10^{-3} \text{ m})^4}{4}$$

$$= 4.81 \times 10^{-7} \text{ m}^4$$

Removing the centre of the beam has resulted in a change of less than 10% in the second moment of area, i.e. the resistance of the beam to bending.

SAQ 6.2

The second moment of area of the section about the z-axis is calculated using the formula given in Table 6.1:

$$I_z = \frac{bh^3}{12} - 2\left(\frac{cd^3}{12}\right)$$

$$= \frac{0.30 \text{ m} \times (0.45 \text{ m})^3}{12} - 2 \times \frac{0.14 \text{ m} \times (0.39 \text{ m})^3}{12}$$

$$= 8.94 \times 10^{-4} \text{ m}^4$$

The stress is calculated using the engineer's bending equation (Equation 6.9).

(a) The maximum bending stress in the web occurs at the extremes of the web, just next to the flanges. So, the stress at top of the web, i.e. at $y = (450 \text{ mm}/2) - 30 \text{ mm} = 195 \text{ mm}$, is:

$$\sigma_x = \frac{My}{I_z} = \frac{200 \times 10^3 \text{ N m} \times 195 \times 10^{-3} \text{ m}}{8.94 \times 10^{-4} \text{ m}^4} = 43.6 \times 10^6 \text{ Pa} = 43.6 \text{ MPa}$$

(b) The maximum stress in the flange occurs at the outer surfaces, i.e. at $y = 450 \text{ mm}/2 = 225 \text{ mm}$:

$$\sigma_x = \frac{200 \times 10^3 \text{ N m} \times 225 \times 10^{-3} \text{ m}}{8.94 \times 10^{-4} \text{ m}^4} = 50.3 \text{ MPa}$$

SAQ 6.3

The second moment of area of the ungrooved beam with rectangular cross section is:

$$I_z = \frac{bH^3}{12} = \frac{40\times10^{-3}\text{ m}\times\left(100\times10^{-3}\text{ m}\right)^3}{12} = 3.33\times10^{-6}\text{ m}^4$$

The maximum bending stress at $y = H/2 = 50$ mm:

$$\sigma_x = \frac{My}{I_z}$$

$$= \frac{300\text{ N m}\times50\times10^{-3}\text{ m}}{3.33\times10^{-6}\text{ m}^4}$$

$$= 4.5\times10^6\text{ Pa}$$

$$= 4.5\text{ MPa}$$

For a groove depth of $2r = 10$ mm, the reduced cross-sectional height $h = H - 4r$ = 80 mm. The stress concentration factors for this geometry are given in Figure 6.29(b). For $H/h = 100/80 = 1.25$ and $r/h = 5/80 = 0.0625$, I read from the chart $K_b = 2.5$. To calculate the stress, I need to calculate the second moment of area of the grooved beam using the critical (reduced) cross-sectional height of 80 mm:

$$I_z = \frac{bh^3}{12} = \frac{40\times10^{-3}\text{ m}\times\left(80\times10^{-3}\text{ m}\right)^3}{12} = 1.71\times10^{-6}\text{ m}^4$$

The maximum stress at the reduced section is when $y = h/2 = 40$ mm:

$$\sigma_x = K_b\frac{My}{I_z}$$

$$= 2.5\times\frac{300\text{ N m}\times40\times10^{-3}\text{ m}}{1.71\times10^{-6}\text{ m}^4}$$

$$= 17.5\text{ MPa}$$

That means an increase in stress by a factor of $17.5/4.5 \approx 4$.

For an increased groove depth of $2r = 25$ mm, the reduced cross-sectional height h = $H - 4r = 50$ mm. The stress concentration factors for this geometry are given in Figure 6.29(b). For $H/h = 100/50 = 2$ and $r/h = 12.5/50 = 0.25$, K_b is 1.64 from Figure 6.29(b). The second moment of area of the grooved beam using the cross-sectional height of 50 mm is:

$$I_z = \frac{bh^3}{12} = \frac{40\times10^{-3}\text{ m}\times\left(50\times10^{-3}\text{ m}\right)^3}{12} = 0.417\times10^{-6}\text{ m}^4$$

The maximum stress at the reduced section is when $y = h/2 = 25$ mm:

$$\sigma_x = K_b\frac{My}{I_z}$$

$$= 1.64\times\frac{300\text{ N m}\times25\times10^{-3}\text{ m}}{0.417\times10^{-6}\text{ m}^4}$$

$$= 29.5\text{ MPa}$$

So, the increase in stress compared with the ungrooved beam is $29.5/4.5 \approx 7$ times.

SAQ 6.4

The free-body diagrams are shown in Figure 6.103.

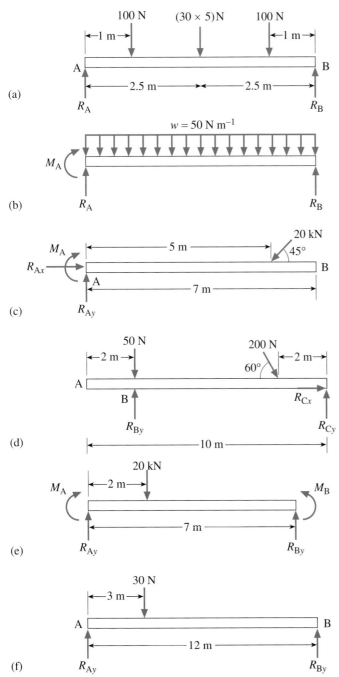

Figure 6.103   Free-body diagrams of the beams in Figure 6.37

(a) Statically determinate: two unknowns (excluding the horizontal reaction at B, which should be zero as there are no horizontal forces acting on the beam).

Taking moments about A:

$$\sum M_A = 0$$

$$-(100 \text{ N} \times 1 \text{ m}) - (150 \text{ N} \times 2.5 \text{ m}) - (100 \text{ N} \times 4 \text{ m}) + (R_B \times 5 \text{ m}) = 0$$

Therefore:

$$R_B = \frac{100\ \text{N} + 375\ \text{N} + 400\ \text{N}}{5} = 175\ \text{N}$$

Equilibrium in the vertical (y-direction) gives:

$$\sum F_y = 0$$
$$R_A - 100\ \text{N} - 150\ \text{N} - 100\ \text{N} + 175\ \text{N} = 0$$

Therefore:

$$R_A = 175\ \text{N}$$

(b) Statically indeterminate: three unknowns (excluding the horizontal reaction at A, which is zero), but only two equilibrium equations.

(c) Statically determinate: three unknowns (including the horizontal reaction at A) and three equilibrium equations.

Taking moments about A:

$$\sum M_A = 0$$
$$-M_A - \left(20\ \text{kN} \times \cos 45° \times 5\ \text{m}\right) = 0$$

So:

$$M_A = -70.7\ \text{kN m}$$

Equilibrium in the y-direction gives:

$$\sum F_y = 0$$
$$R_{Ay} - 20\ \text{kN} \times \cos 45° = 0$$

Therefore:

$$R_{Ay} = 14.14\ \text{kN}$$

Equilibrium in the x-direction gives:

$$\sum F_x = 0$$
$$R_{Ax} - 20\ \text{kN} \times \cos 45° = 0$$

Therefore:

$$R_{Ax} = 14.14\ \text{kN}$$

(d) Statically determinate: three unknowns (including the horizontal reaction at C).

Taking moments about B:

$$\sum M_B = 0$$
$$-\left(200\ \text{N} \times \sin 60° \times 6\ \text{m}\right) + \left(R_{Cy} \times 8\ \text{m}\right) = 0$$

Therefore:

$$R_{Cy} = \frac{1040\ \text{N}}{8} = 130\ \text{N}$$

Equilibrium in the y-direction gives:

$$\sum F_y = 0$$

$$R_{By} + 130\ \text{N} - 50\ \text{N} - 200\ \text{N} \times \sin 60° = 0$$

Therefore:

$$R_{By} = 223\ \text{N} - 130\ \text{N} = 93\ \text{N}$$

Equilibrium in the x-direction gives:

$$\sum F_x = 0$$

$$200\ \text{N} \times \cos 60° + R_{Cx} = 0$$

Therefore:

$$R_{Cx} = -100\ \text{N}$$

(e) Statically indeterminate: four unknowns (excluding the horizontal reactions at A and B).

(f) Unstable structure: there is no horizontal constraint; therefore, even though there is no horizontal force acting on the beam, this is a mechanism.

SAQ 6.5

Taking moments about A:

$$-W \times a + R_{By} \times L = 0$$

Thus:

$$R_{By} = \frac{Wa}{L}$$

Equilibrium in the y-direction gives:

$$R_{Ay} + R_{By} - W = 0$$

Therefore:

$$\begin{aligned} R_{Ay} &= W - \frac{Wa}{L} \\ &= \frac{W}{L}(L - a) \\ &= \frac{Wb}{L} \end{aligned}$$

SAQ 6.6

(a) From symmetry, both support reactions can be calculated as W.

(b) The three imaginary cuts I made are shown in Figure 6.104. I will now use the equilibrium equations to solve for each case.

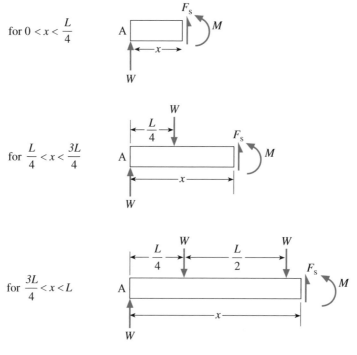

for $0 < x < \dfrac{L}{4}$

for $\dfrac{L}{4} < x < \dfrac{3L}{4}$

for $\dfrac{3L}{4} < x < L$

Figure 6.104   Free-body diagrams for the beam in Figure 6.45

(i) For $0 < x < L/4$

Equilibrium in the y-direction gives:

$F_s = -W$

Taking moments about the cut face:

$M = Wx$

(ii) For $L/4 < x < 3L/4$

Equilibrium in the y-direction gives:

$W - W + F_s = 0$

Therefore:

$F_s = 0$

Taking moments about the cut face:

$-Wx + W\left(x - \dfrac{L}{4}\right) + M = 0$

Thus:

$M = Wx - Wx + \dfrac{WL}{4}$

Therefore:

$M = \dfrac{WL}{4}$

(iii) For $3L/4 < x < L$

Equilibrium in the y-direction gives:

$W - W - W + F_s = 0$

Therefore:

$F_s = W$

Taking moments about the cut face:

$$-Wx + W\left(x - \frac{L}{4}\right) + W\left(x - \frac{3L}{4}\right) + M = 0$$

Hence:

$M = WL - Wx$

$\quad = W(L - x)$

(c) The shear-force and bending-moment diagrams are constructed as seen in Figure 6.105. Between the loading points, the shear force is zero and the bending moment is constant. Thus, by using this configuration, a large proportion of the beam may be subjected to a uniform bending moment; for this reason, four-point loading is often used in laboratory tests for the investigation of material properties.

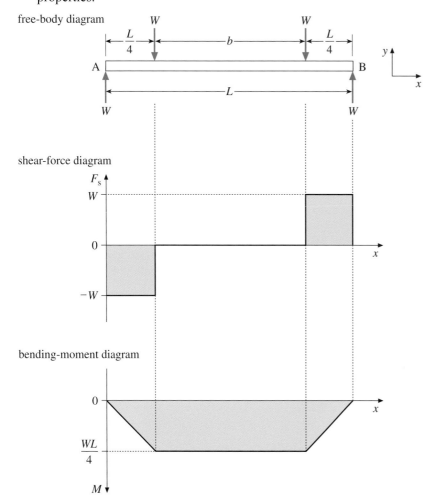

Figure 6.105 Shear-force and bending-moment diagrams for the beams in Figure 6.45

SAQ 6.7

The second moment of area for the section is obtained using the formula given in Table 6.1:

$$I = \frac{bh^3}{12} - \frac{b_i h_i^3}{12}$$

$$= \frac{25 \times 10^{-3} \text{ m} \times \left(25 \times 10^{-3} \text{ m}\right)^3}{12} - \frac{21 \times 10^{-3} \text{ m} \times \left(21 \times 10^{-3} \text{ m}\right)^3}{12}$$

$$= 1.635 \times 10^{-8} \text{ m}^4$$

For the case where the load is uniformly distributed along the width of the shoe, we obtained the maximum bending moment in the example as 60.9 N m. The magnitude of maximum stress, which occurs at the maximum distance from the neutral axis, i.e. $y = 12.5$ mm, is given by the engineer's bending theory:

$$\sigma_x = \frac{My}{I}$$

$$= \frac{60.9 \text{ N m} \times 12.5 \times 10^{-3} \text{ m}}{1.635 \times 10^{-8} \text{ m}^4}$$

$$= 46.6 \text{ MPa}$$

The stress at the upper part would be −46.6 MPa, and at the lower part it would be +46.6 MPa.

The assumption of a point load, instead of the load being distributed over the width of the shoe, is a 'worst case'; the maximum bending moment was calculated in the example as 70.9 N m. This gives a maximum stress of:

$$\sigma_x = \frac{My}{I}$$

$$= \frac{70.9 \text{ N m} \times 12.5 \times 10^{-3} \text{ m}}{1.635 \times 10^{-8} \text{ m}^4}$$

$$= 54.2 \text{ MPa}$$

SAQ 6.8

The worst possible case of loading for a rung is as a simply supported beam with the whole load concentrated at the middle point of the rung (see Exercise 6.9). The bending moment for that case is obtained by using the formula in Figure 6.43:

$$M = \frac{Wab}{L}$$

where L is the distance between the *supports* and a and b are the distances between the point of application of the load and the left- and right-hand supports respectively (Figure 6.106). The bending moment is a maximum when $a = b = L/2$, thus:

$$M = \frac{W \times (L/2) \times (L/2)}{L}$$

$$= \frac{WL}{4}$$

$$= \frac{(175 \times 9.81) \text{ N} \times 0.36 \text{ m}}{4}$$

$$= 154.5 \text{ N m}$$

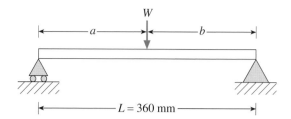

Figure 6.106   Timber ladder rung as a simply supported beam subject to a point load

The maximum stress in the rung may be determined by the engineer's bending equation:

$$\sigma_x = \frac{My}{I}$$

The second moment of area for a solid circular cross section is obtained from the formula given in Table 6.1:

$$I = \frac{\pi r^4}{4}$$

The maximum stress in the rung's cross sections occurs at $y = r$. The stress equation can then be rewritten as:

$$\sigma_x = \frac{My}{I} = \frac{Mr}{\left(\dfrac{\pi r^4}{4}\right)} = \frac{4M}{\pi r^3} \tag{6.39}$$

We would like the stress in the rung not to exceed the maximum allowable stress of 70 MPa. So, a minimum radius for the rung can be calculated by rearranging Equation (6.39) and setting $\sigma_x = 70$ MPa:

$$r = \left(\frac{4M}{\pi \sigma_x}\right)^{1/3} = \left(\frac{4 \times 154.4 \text{ N m}}{\pi \times 70 \times 10^6 \text{ Pa}}\right)^{1/3} = 14.4 \times 10^{-3} \text{ m} = 14.1 \text{ mm}$$

Thus, a minimum diameter for the rung should be 14.1 mm × 2 = 28.2 mm.

For a load factor of 2, we must repeat the calculations for the applied load of $175 \times 2 = 350$ kg, which gives the maximum bending moment as 308.7 N m. Then the minimum radius is given by:

$$r = \left(\frac{4M}{\pi \sigma_x}\right)^{1/3} = \left(\frac{4 \times 308.7 \text{ N m}}{\pi \times 70 \times 10^6 \text{ Pa}}\right)^{1/3} = 17.8 \times 10^{-3} \text{ m} = 17.8 \text{ mm}$$

The minimum rung diameter is then 17.8 mm × 2 = 35.6 mm.

SAQ 6.9

The reaction forces for this symmetrical loading are $R_A = R_B = 170$ kN. We need imaginary cuts before and after the point load; the free-body diagrams are given in Figure 6.107.

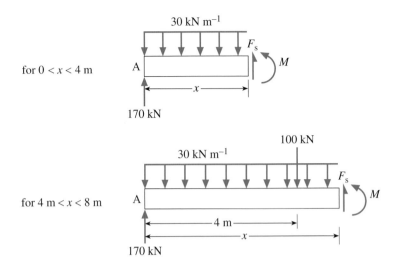

for $0 < x < 4$ m

for 4 m $< x < 8$ m

Figure 6.107   Free-body diagrams for the beam in Figure 6.56

1   For $0 < x < 4$ m

Equilibrium in the y-direction gives:

$$170 - 30x + F_s = 0$$

Thus:

$$F_s = 30x - 170$$

Taking moments about the cut face:

$$-170 \times x + 30x \times \frac{x}{2} + M = 0$$

Therefore:

$$M = -15x^2 + 170x$$

2   For 4 m $< x < 8$ m

Equilibrium in the y-direction gives:

$$170 - 30x - 100 + F_s = 0$$

So:

$$F_s = 30x - 70$$

Taking moments about the cut face:

$$-170 \times x + 30x \times \frac{x}{2} + 100 \times (x - 4) + M = 0$$

Therefore:

$$M = -15x^2 + 70x + 400$$

The shear-force and bending-moment diagrams are plotted in Figure 6.108.

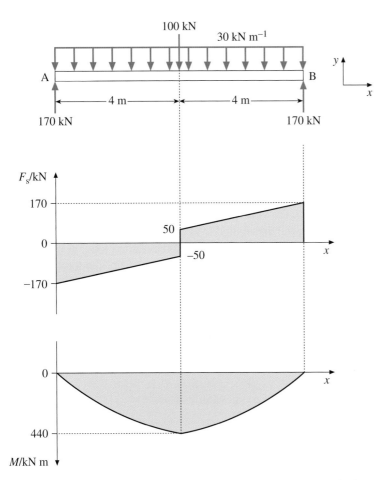

Figure 6.108 Shear-force and bending-moment diagrams for the beams in Figure 6.56

The shear-force and bending-moment diagrams for the simply supported beam subjected to a point load plus a UDL are essentially a combination of those diagrams for a beam subjected to a point load (Figure 6.43) and a beam subjected to a UDL (Figure 6.49) separately.

SAQ 6.10

For the I-beam, the second moment of area is:

$$I_z = \frac{bh^3}{12} - 2\frac{cd^3}{12}$$

$$= \frac{0.15 \text{ m} \times (0.2 \text{ m})^3}{12} - 2 \times \frac{0.06 \text{ m} \times (0.14 \text{ m})^3}{12}$$

$$= 7.26 \times 10^{-5} \text{ m}^4$$

The maximum shear stress in the I-beam occurs in the web as given by Equation (6.16):

$$\tau_{max} = \frac{F_s}{A_{web}} = \frac{30 \times 10^3 \text{ N}}{0.03 \text{ m} \times 0.14 \text{ m}} = 7.1 \times 10^6 \text{ Pa} = 7.1 \text{ MPa}$$

The maximum bending moment in a cantilever is given as $M_{max} = WL$; therefore, the maximum bending stress in the I-beam is calculated as:

$$\sigma_{max} = \frac{M_{max}\, y}{I_z} = \frac{\left(30\times10^3 \text{ N}\times3 \text{ m}\right)\times(0.2 \text{ m}/2)}{7.26\times10^{-5} \text{ m}^4} = 124\times10^6 \text{ Pa} = 124 \text{ MPa}$$

Again, the shear stress in the beam is negligible in comparison to the maximum bending stress.

SAQ 6.11

The maximum bending moment should occur at the fixed end of the horizontal cantilever, where it is attached to the vertical support. For the purpose of determining the maximum bending moment, the distributed load can be replaced by an equivalent concentrated load acting at the centre of the area of the distributed load, as shown in Figure 6.109. Assuming the cantilever is subjected to one half of the total design weight, the maximum bending moment at the fixed end is:

$$M_{max} = -WL$$
$$= -mgL$$
$$= -\left(180 \text{ kg}\times9.81 \text{ m s}^{-2}\times0.28 \text{ m}\right)$$
$$= -494 \text{ N m}$$

The second moment of area of the horizontal cantilever is:

$$I = \frac{bh^3}{12} = \frac{40\times10^{-3} \text{ m}\times\left(60\times10^{-3} \text{ m}\right)^3}{12} = 7.2\times10^{-7} \text{ m}^4$$

Then, the maximum stress in the horizontal cantilever is at $y = \pm h/2 = 30$ mm, so:

$$\sigma_{max} = \frac{M_{max}\, y}{I_z}$$
$$= \frac{-494 \text{ N m}\times(\pm30\times10^{-3} \text{ m})}{7.2\times10^{-7} \text{ m}^4}$$
$$= \pm20.6\times10^6 \text{ Pa}$$
$$= \pm20.6 \text{ MPa}$$

This is considerably lower than the maximum allowable stress of 67 MPa.

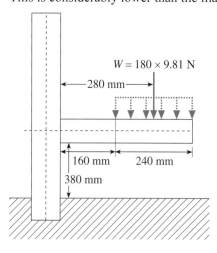

$W = 180 \times 9.81$ N

280 mm

160 mm   240 mm

380 mm

Figure 6.109   Schematic of one of the bench supports showing the distributed load as an equivalent point load

SAQ 6.12

The forces acting on the vertical support can be represented by a vertical force equal to W acting on the centroidal axis of the support plus a bending moment about the joint, with a magnitude W times the moment arm, as shown in Figure 6.70. Note that the moment arm in this case is taken from the line of action of the sitter's weight to the centroidal axis of the vertical support.

Since this bending moment is directly imposed on the support, but not a result of a transverse load on the beam, it is constant in the support all the way from the joint to ground. The magnitude of this bending moment is:

$$
\begin{aligned}
M_{max} &= -WL \\
&= -mgL \\
&= -\left(180 \text{ kg} \times 9.81 \text{ m s}^{-2} \times 0.32 \text{ m}\right) \\
&= -565 \text{ N m}
\end{aligned}
$$

The second moment of area of the vertical support is:

$$
I = \frac{bh^3}{12} = \frac{60 \times 10^{-3} \text{ m} \times \left(80 \times 10^{-3} \text{ m}\right)^3}{12} = 2.56 \times 10^{-6} \text{ m}^4
$$

The maximum bending stress in the vertical support is at $y = \pm h/2 = 40$ mm:

$$
\begin{aligned}
\sigma_x &= \frac{M_{max} y}{I_z} \\
&= \frac{-565 \text{ N m} \times (\pm 40 \times 10^{-3} \text{ m})}{2.56 \times 10^{-6} \text{ m}^4} \\
&= \pm 8.8 \times 10^6 \text{ Pa} \\
&= \pm 8.8 \text{ MPa}
\end{aligned}
$$

Since there are combined bending and axial loads on the support, we also need to consider the direct axial stress due to compressive force W. The direct stress is:

$$
\begin{aligned}
\sigma_x &= \frac{W}{A} \\
&= \frac{(-180 \times 9.81) \text{ N}}{60 \times 10^{-3} \text{ m} \times 80 \times 10^{-3} \text{ m}} \\
&= -0.37 \times 10^6 \text{ Pa} \\
&= -0.37 \text{ MPa}
\end{aligned}
$$

The axial stress is very small compared with the bending stresses. Nevertheless, superposition of bending and axial stresses gives -0.37 MPa $- 8.8$ MPa $= -9.17$ MPa on the inner (cantilever) side of the support and -0.37 MPa $+ 8.8$ MPa $= 8.43$ MPa on the outside edge of the support.

SAQ 6.13

The pole can be modelled as a cantilever with a point load at its free end (Figure 6.110).

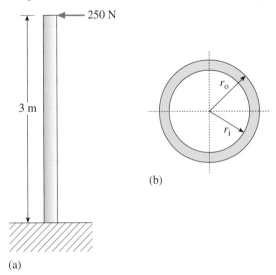

(b)

(a)

Figure 6.110   (a) Satellite-dish pole; (b) cross section of the pole

The second moment of area for the cross section of the 60 mm diameter pole ($r_o = 30$ mm and $t_{wall} = 3$ mm) can be calculated using the formula in Table 6.1 for a hollow circular section:

$$I = \frac{\pi}{4}\left(r_o^4 - r_i^4\right)$$

$$= \frac{\pi\left[\left(30\times10^{-3}\text{ m}\right)^4 - \left(27\times10^{-3}\text{ m}\right)^4\right]}{4}$$

$$= 2.188\times10^{-7}\text{ m}^4$$

The tip deflection of the pole is determined by the formula in Table 6.2 for the point-loaded cantilever:

$$v = \frac{FL^3}{3EI} = \frac{250\text{ N}\times\left(3\text{ m}\right)^3}{3\times210\times10^9\text{ Pa}\times2.188\times10^{-7}\text{ m}^4} = 49\times10^{-3}\text{ m} = 49\text{ mm}$$

This deflection is higher than the maximum allowable value of 20 mm.

For the 80 mm diameter pole, the second moment of area is:

$$I = \frac{\pi}{4}\left(r_o^4 - r_i^4\right)$$

$$= \frac{\pi\left[\left(40\times10^{-3}\text{ m}\right)^4 - \left(37\times10^{-3}\text{ m}\right)^4\right]}{4}$$

$$= 5.39\times10^{-7}\text{ m}^4$$

The tip deflection of the pole is determined by the formula in Table 6.2 for the point-loaded cantilever:

$$v = \frac{FL^3}{3EI} = \frac{250\ \text{N} \times (3\ \text{m})^3}{3 \times 210 \times 10^9\ \text{Pa} \times 5.39 \times 10^{-7}\ \text{m}^4} = 19.9 \times 10^{-3}\ \text{m} = 19.9\ \text{mm}$$

which may be acceptable.

SAQ 6.14

(a) $J = \frac{1}{2}\pi\left(r_o^4 - r_i^4\right) = \frac{\pi}{2}\left[\left(12.5 \times 10^{-3}\ \text{m}\right)^4 - \left(10 \times 10^{-3}\ \text{m}\right)^4\right] = 2.264 \times 10^{-8}\ \text{m}^4$

(b) $T = \frac{GJ\theta}{L} = \frac{30 \times 10^9\ \text{Pa} \times 2.264 \times 10^{-8}\ \text{m}^4 \times 0.4\ \text{rad}}{5\ \text{m}} = 54.3\ \text{N m}$

(c) $\gamma = \frac{r\theta}{L} = \frac{12.5 \times 10^{-3}\ \text{m} \times 0.4\ \text{rad}}{5\ \text{m}} = 0.001$

SAQ 6.15

The maximum shear stress in a shaft subjected to a torque can be calculated using Equation (6.29):

$$\tau_{max} = \frac{Tr_{max}}{J}$$

Each portion of the shaft is subjected to the same torque. We need the polar second moment of area of each section; for the hollow tube A it is:

$$J_A = \frac{1}{2}\pi\left(r_o^4 - r_i^4\right) = \frac{\pi}{2}\left[\left(30 \times 10^{-3}\ \text{m}\right)^4 - \left(20 \times 10^{-3}\ \text{m}\right)^4\right] = 1.02 \times 10^{-6}\ \text{m}^4$$

For the solid section B:

$$J_B = \frac{1}{2}\pi r^4 = \frac{\pi}{2} \times \left(25 \times 10^{-3}\ \text{m}\right)^4 = 0.614 \times 10^{-6}\ \text{m}^4$$

The maximum shear stress in the hollow section is at $r_{max} = 30$ mm:

$$\tau_{max} = \frac{Tr_{max}}{J_A} = \frac{1000\ \text{N m} \times 30 \times 10^{-3}\ \text{m}}{1.02 \times 10^{-6}\ \text{m}^4} = 29.4 \times 10^6\ \text{Pa} = 29.4\ \text{MPa}$$

The maximum stress in the solid section is at $r_{max} = 25$ mm:

$$\tau_{max} = \frac{Tr_{max}}{J_B} = \frac{1000\ \text{N m} \times 25 \times 10^{-3}\ \text{m}}{0.614 \times 10^{-6}\ \text{m}^4} = 40.7\ \text{MPa}$$

The shear stress is greater in the solid section and maximum shear stress is therefore 40.7 MPa.

SAQ 6.16

The torsion equation gives the relation between the torque and the geometry of the shaft:

$$T = \frac{\tau J}{r}$$

The polar moment of area of a solid circular shaft is:

$$J = \frac{\pi r^4}{2}$$

So:

$$T = \frac{\tau}{r}\frac{\pi r^4}{2} = \tau\frac{\pi r^3}{2}$$

(a) Doubling the diameter increases the torque $2^3 = 8$ times.

(b) No change. The torque is independent of the length.

(c) A 50% higher yield stress means that the shaft can carry a higher torque. As the torque is proportional to the stress, this just means a 50% higher torque can be carried.

SAQ 6.17

The shoulder fillet at the section change causes a stress concentration, which increases the maximum shear stress in the shaft with the smaller diameter by a factor K_{tr}. The second polar moment of area for the shaft with the smaller diameter is:

$$J = \frac{1}{2}\pi r^4 = \frac{\pi}{2}\times\left(25\times10^{-3}\text{ m}\right)^4 = 6.14\times10^{-7}\text{ m}^4$$

The stress concentration factor K_{tr} is found from the graph given in Figure 6.85. So, for $H/h = 1.6$ and $r/h = 0.2$, K_{tr} is read from the graph as 1.225. The torsion formula with stress concentration (Equation 6.30) gives:

$$\tau_{max} = K_{tr}\frac{Tr_{max}}{J} = 1.225\times\frac{1000\text{ N m}\times25\times10^{-3}\text{ m}}{6.14\times10^{-7}\text{ m}^4} = 49.9\text{ MPa}$$

which is higher than the maximum allowable stress. So, either the design of the shaft should be changed (a larger-diameter shaft and/or a larger fillet radius) or a stronger shaft material should be chosen.

SAQ 6.18

(a) We can estimate the buckling load using the Euler formula (Equation 6.34). First, we need to calculate the second moment of area of the rod. From Table 6.1, for a circular cross section:

$$I = \frac{\pi r^4}{4} = \frac{\pi\times\left(10\times10^{-3}\right)^4}{4} = 7.85\times10^{-9}\text{ m}^4$$

Then, applying the Euler formula gives:

$$F_{crit} = \frac{\pi^2 EI}{L^2} = \frac{\pi^2\times70\times10^9\text{ Pa}\times7.85\times10^{-9}\text{ m}^4}{\left(2.4\text{ m}\right)^2} = 942\text{ N}$$

(b) The safety factor for buckling is the ratio between the critical load and the service load, i.e.:

$$\text{safety factor} = \frac{F_{crit}}{F_{appl}} = \frac{942}{400} \approx 2.4$$

(c) We can use the Euler formula (Equation 6.34) again to determine the *critical diameter* of the rod that would buckle at $F_{crit} = 400$ N. The second moment of area of the rod with the critical radius is:

$$I = \frac{F_{crit} L^2}{\pi^2 E} = \frac{400 \text{ N} \times (2.4 \text{ m})^2}{\pi^2 \times 70 \times 10^9 \text{ Pa}} = 3.34 \times 10^{-9} \text{ m}^4$$

Substituting this new I into the second moment of area equation:

$$I = \frac{\pi r^4}{4} = 3.34 \times 10^{-9} \text{ m}^4$$

Therefore:

$$r = \left(\frac{4I}{\pi} \right)^{1/4}$$

$$= \left(\frac{4 \times 3.34 \times 10^{-9}}{\pi} \right)^{1/4}$$

$$= 8.1 \times 10^{-3} \text{ m}$$

$$= 8.1 \text{ mm}$$

So, the critical diameter is 16.2 mm.

SAQ 6.19

The design load for the column is the applied load times the load factor, i.e. 5 kN × 5 = 25 kN. The restraint factor is $K = 2$ for one end fixed and the other end hinged (Figure 6.97c). We find the minimum dimensions for the plank by taking the design load as the critical buckling load in Euler's formula (with restraint factor, Equation 6.35), i.e.:

$$F_{design} = F_{crit} = \frac{K\pi^2 EI}{L^2} = 25 \text{ kN}$$

The second moment area of the section which satisfies this equation is then found by rearranging it as:

$$I = \frac{F_{design} L^2}{K\pi^2 E} = \frac{25 \times 10^3 \text{ N} \times (7 \text{ m})^2}{2 \times \pi^2 \times 10 \times 10^9 \text{ Pa}} = 6.206 \times 10^{-6} \text{ m}^4$$

The second moment of area for a rectangular section is given as:

$$I = \frac{bh^3}{12}$$

We do not know whether the plank would deflect in the direction of its given width (100 mm) or the required thickness. In other words, which one is 100 mm: b or h?

We know that the buckling deflection in rectangular sections occurs preferentially in the direction of smaller cross-sectional dimension (recall the buckling of a plastic ruler in Figure 6.92). So, the height h (or thickness) should be smaller than the width b.

So, assuming the 100 mm is the bigger dimension, and therefore assigning it to b, we calculate h by rearranging the second moment of area equation:

$$h^3 = \frac{12 \times I}{b}$$

$$h = \left(\frac{12 \times 6.206 \times 10^{-6} \text{ m}^4}{0.1 \text{ m}} \right)^{1/3}$$

$$= 90.6 \times 10^{-3} \text{ m}$$

$$= 90.6 \text{ mm}$$

Since $h = 90.6$ mm is smaller than the 100 mm width, our assumption seems to be correct, and this is the minimum thickness of the plank.

SAQ 6.20

In this case the strut is constrained to bend about the y-axis (Figure 6.101), so the solution to this problem is similar to the one that was given in the example, except that the radius of gyration r_y for bending about the y-axis must be used here:

$$r_y = \sqrt{\frac{I_y}{A}} = \sqrt{\frac{9.01 \times 10^{-8} \text{ m}^4}{2.84 \times 10^{-4} \text{ m}^2}} = 17.88 \times 10^{-3} \text{ m}$$

The critical buckling stress then becomes:

$$\sigma_{\text{crit}} = \frac{K\pi^2 E}{(L/r)^2}$$

$$= \frac{1 \times \pi^2 \times 200 \times 10^9 \text{ Pa}}{(0.5 \text{ m}/0.01788 \text{ m})^2}$$

$$= 2.524 \times 10^9 \text{ Pa}$$

$$= 2.524 \text{ GPa}$$

This is greater than the proof stress of the steel in compression (1000 MPa), so we conclude that this strut will fail by yielding. The failure load F_{yield} will be:

$$F_{\text{yield}} = \sigma_{\text{yield}} \times A$$

$$= 1000 \times 10^6 \text{ Pa} \times 2.84 \times 10^{-4} \text{ m}^2$$

$$= 284 \times 10^3 \text{ N}$$

$$= 284 \text{ kN}$$

ACKNOWLEDGEMENTS

Grateful acknowledgement is made to the following sources:

FIGURES

Figure 6.2: Courtesy of Building Research Establishment.

Figure 6.3(a): David Williams/Alamy.

Figure 6.3(b): Mark Zybler/Alamy.

Figure 6.5(a): Courtesy of Mark Kavanagh at http://ktransit.com

Figure 6.6(a): Courtesy of www.undiscoveredscotland.co.uk

Figure 6.9(b): G P Bowater/Alamy.

Figure 6.9(c): Courtesy of US Bureau of Reclamation.

Figure 6.9(d): Courtesy of Rolls-Royce plc.

Figure 6.11: © PhotoDisc.

Figure 6.16: © The Print Collector/Alamy.

Figure 6.18: From a bust at the École des Ponts et Chauseés www-history.mcs.st-andrews.ac.uk

Figure 6.26: © Bettmann/Corbis.

Figure 6.28(a): Dr Jeremy Burgess/Science Photo Library.

Figure 6.33(a) and 6.33(b): Courtesy of James Baughn at www.bridgehunter.com

Figure 6.44(a): © Pixonnet.com/Alamy.

Figure 6.44(b): Taken from www.flmvpa.org

Figure 6.44(c): © Ole Graf/zefa/Corbis.

Figure 6.44(d): © Royal Geographical Society/Alamy.

Figure 6.46: © Duomo/Corbis.

Figure 6.89(a): © Rex Features.

Figure 6.89(b): © Randy Faris/Corbis.

Figure 6.89(c): Courtesy of www.teammahaska.org

Figure 6.94: © NorthWind Picture Archives/Alamy.

Every effort has been made to contact copyright holders. If any have been inadvertently overlooked the publishers will be pleased to make the necessary arrangements at the first opportunity.

COURSE TEAM ACKNOWLEDGEMENTS

This part was prepared for the course team by Salih Gungor.

PART 7
RESIDUAL STRESS

CONTENTS

1 INTRODUCTION

So far in this course we have been concerned primarily with stresses arising from externally applied forces and loads. The one exception we have covered is internal stresses that are generated when a component is constrained so that it cannot expand or contract in response to a temperature change.

Stresses can exist within a component or assembly in the absence of any externally applied load or self-load. Such stresses are termed *residual stresses*, and thermal effects are just one way in which they can be generated. Residual stresses can be produced by forming, joining, machining, heat treatment, abrasion, impact and many other relatively simple processes that materials and components are subjected to during fabrication. Residual stresses can be thought of as 'locked-in' stresses within a component.

Residual stresses can have the same effects on a material as stresses generated by applied loads; hence, they need to be understood and quantified in the same way as those external stresses. It is important to appreciate that residual stresses act in addition to in-service stresses. They can add to a stress caused by an applied load to cause yield, for example, even though the applied load itself was not high enough to do so. Consequently, residual stresses can cause premature failure. They can affect dynamic failure mechanisms such as fatigue and can drive processes such as stress-corrosion cracking. You will see more of the effects of residual stresses in Block 2.

On the other hand, residual stresses can also be beneficial, as compressive residual stress can act against applied tensile loading and thereby reduce the likelihood of failure. Indeed, there are many processes that are designed specifically to generate compressive residual stresses in a particular region of a component, which can increase the component's resistance to an externally applied load (as in ☑ **prestressed concrete** ☑) or extend its service life (see ☑ **Peening for life improvement** ☑).

☑ Prestressed concrete

Some materials, such as concrete, are poor at carrying tensile forces and, therefore, it is better to ensure that they are loaded in compression. However, not all buildings can afford to have arches to minimize the tensile loading within them, and in any case we are all familiar with concrete structures where some of the internal forces are clearly tensile (Figure 7.1).

Figure 7.1   A concrete structure experiencing tensile forces

A simple solution is to add steel reinforcing bars: steel is much better at carrying tensile forces.

EXERCISE 7.1

Where should the steel bars be placed in a reinforced concrete beam that will be loaded in bending?

However, although adding a steel reinforcement to concrete to make a composite material in this way may reduce the tensile load in the concrete, it won't reduce it to zero. The trick is to engineer the concrete to have a compressive residual stress within it. This is done as shown in Figure 7.2.

First, steel bars are loaded and held in tension. Concrete is then cast in place around the tensioned bars. Once the concrete has set, the load on the

bars is removed and the elastic strain within them relaxes. However, as the bars contract from their tensioned state, they exert a force on the surrounding concrete, pushing it into compression. The result is that in the final material the concrete around the steel bars is compressed, with some residual tension in the steel. When the reinforced concrete is loaded, the residual compressive stress within it acts against the tensile force from the loading, so the concrete does not experience a resultant tensile stress.

Thorough analysis of the bending of a prestressed beam is, as you might expect, more difficult than for a beam made of a conventional, homogeneous material. In addition to the variation in stiffness caused by the inclusion of the steel bars, the internal stresses can shift the position of the neutral surface during bending; but I won't go into the mathematical details here.

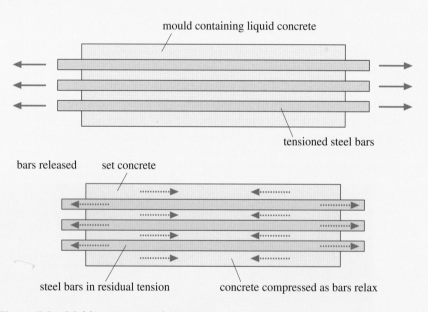

Figure 7.2   Making prestressed concrete

☑ Peening for life improvement

Metal fatigue is a phenomenon of progressive crack growth in a material as a result of oscillating loading, where the applied loads are significantly lower than would normally be expected to cause failure. In Block 2 you will study fatigue in more detail.

The fatigue life of a material can be greatly improved by reducing the tensile loads it experiences. So, as with prestressed concrete, engineering a compressive stress into the material would seem to be a good idea.

EXERCISE 7.2

If a simple beam is subjected to bending, where will the peak tensile stress be found?   ◩

In the majority of loaded components, stress will either be evenly distributed or be concentrated in a particular region because of bending forces or a stress concentrator. In particular, bending stresses are highest at the surfaces, so finding a way to ensure that the surfaces are in residual compression to resist tension from applied loading would be a good thing.

Shot peening

One way this is achieved is by a process called *shot peening*. Small balls, usually made of metal or glass, are fired at the surface of a sample at high speed. As each ball hits, it will deform the surface, producing a small dimple (Figure 7.3a). Essentially, this involves yield and plastic deformation of the surface by the compressive stress of the impact. When the material below the yielded zone relaxes elastically after the impact, it pushes the surface material into compression (Figure 7.3b). The compressive stresses at the surface are typically very high, with a zone of lower tensile stress below (Figure 7.3c).

Shot peening can involve multiple peen operations with different shot 'media' and intensities – where the intensity is a function of the shot velocity and the overall peening time.

A typical residual stress profile from shot peening is shown in Figure 7.4. There is a compressive stress

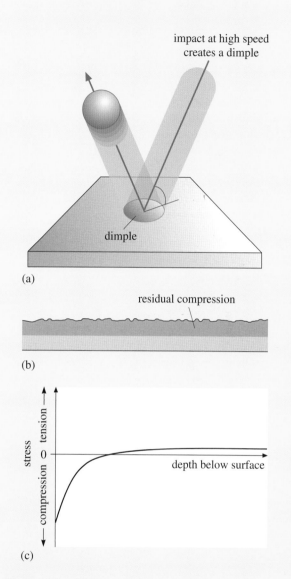

Figure 7.3   (a) Impact of a shot causes a small dimple; (b) the surface is placed into residual compression by the multiple impacts; (c) typical stress profile of a peened sample

up to a depth of around 200 µm, which is balanced by a tensile stress of much smaller magnitude throughout a deeper zone.

The stresses in Figure 7.4 were measured using incremental hole drilling, which can be seen on the course DVD.   ▷

Figure 7.4 Measured residual stress in the two in-plane principal stress directions from a peened magnesium sample, showing that the stress does not vary with direction. Here the stress falls away towards the surface, in contrast to Figure 7.3; the exact profile obtained depends on the material and the peening conditions used

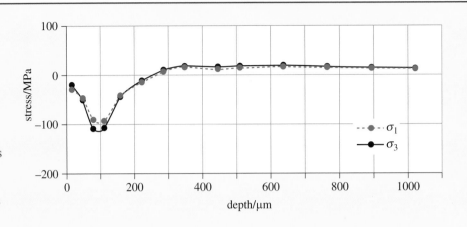

These stresses are found to improve the fatigue life significantly. If you want to know more, stick around for Block 2!

Laser shock peening

Laser shock peening is a relatively new process, where the aim, like that of shot peening, is to create a plastically deformed surface layer in order to produce a compressive residual stress field at the surface.

The first step is to coat the surface of the component with a sacrificial material – often black paint or tape – capable of absorbing laser radiation. The component is then immersed in a material that is transparent to the laser, usually water. The surface is then exposed to a pulse from a high-powered laser. The energy released when the coating absorbs the laser pulse forms a *superheated plasma*, which vaporizes the sacrificial layer. The plasma tries to expand, but it is confined by the layer of water, and hence the expansion causes a mechanical shock wave to be driven into the component. The pressure of this shock wave causes the surface of

the component to deform plastically, producing a compressive residual stress field at the surface in much the same way as shot peening. The process is shown schematically in Figure 7.5.

The advantage of this technique is that the region and magnitude of shock peening can be accurately controlled by the area covered by the laser and by altering the laser's power. Very deep compressive stress regions can be introduced by this method, without some of the associated surface damage that can occur with mechanical peening methods.

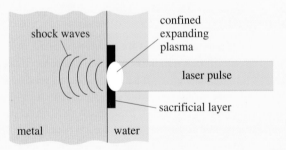

Figure 7.5   The laser shock peening process

The internal forces and moments within a component must be in equilibrium in exactly the same way as for externally applied forces. This means that any residual compressive stress must be balanced by a residual tensile stress. However, a large compressive stress acting over a few hundred micrometres near a surface can be balanced by a much larger zone of very small tensile stress extending over several millimetres.

Residual stresses can occur on a range of length scales, from stresses acting over a few nanometres around a dislocation in a material's atomic lattice, to stresses acting over many tens of metres resulting from the assembly of a large structure. It's possible for a component to contain more than one residual stress field, each from a different origin: for example, a bridge component might have a residual stress acting

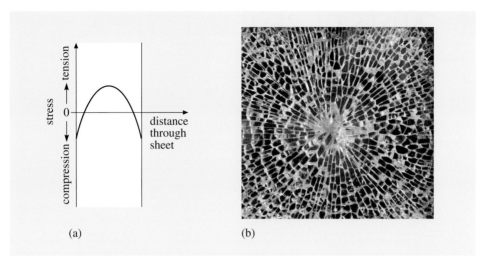

Figure 7.6   (a) Sketch of the residual stress distribution in a thermally toughened glass sheet; (b) the shatter pattern seen in a typical broken toughened-glass panel

over many metres from when it was bent into place for assembly, but also have a local residual stress field of a few millimetres or centimetres around the weld that joins it to the next section.

Residual stresses can have a significant effect on a component, but they are more difficult to predict and to measure than the in-service stresses on which they superimpose. This is because the effects of the residual stresses are not always apparent until the component itself fails. One example of this is thermally toughened glass. Thermally toughened glass has its surfaces cooled rapidly during processing to introduce a compressive residual stress at the surface (Figure 7.6a). Once a crack penetrates the mid-thickness of this type of glass then many cracks can propagate rapidly from this point, driven by the locked-in residual stress within the glass panel, resulting in a characteristic shattered-mosaic pattern (Figure 7.6b).

This part will cover the causes of residual stress, the information needed to analyse residual stresses, the effects of residual stress and the means by which residual stresses can be engineered, measured and controlled.

2 CAUSES OF RESIDUAL STRESS

Fundamentally, residual stresses originate from *shape misfits* between different regions of a component. The basic cause of these misfits is non-uniform strain due to some previous process or treatment. In practice, most non-uniform strains that cause residual stresses arise from plastic deformation. Part of the component is deformed to a different extent from the rest, and elastic relaxation when the deforming force is removed leads to the generation of an elastic residual stress.

Let's think this through in terms of what happens when plastic deformation occurs. The stress–strain behaviour of a simple tensile test specimen is shown schematically in Figure 7.7. If the material is loaded from zero to point B, i.e. a stress above the material's yield point at A, then upon relaxation there will be a residual plastic strain as shown. This means that the material has been permanently deformed. However, there will be no macroscopic residual stress within the specimen in this simple case. This is because uniform deformation took place in the plastically strained section of the specimen and, crucially, the specimen could relax elastically without constraint.

In order to consider how residual stresses are generated, we need to examine a case where only part of the component deforms plastically and the relaxation of the elastic stress is constrained. A good example of such a case is a bar that is deformed in bending to the point where its surfaces become plastically deformed.

Figure 7.8(a) shows a bar with no external forces acting on it. When the bar is bent elastically (Figure 7.8b) there is a variation of stress from tension on one surface to compression on the other, as you've seen many times so far in this course. Removing the applied load allows the bar to relax back to its undeformed state (Figure 7.8a). When the applied load is increased, the material will eventually yield. Plasticity first occurs at the top and bottom surfaces, where the stress is highest, and if the load is increased yet further, the plastic layer spreads to greater depths (I'm assuming for the sake of simplicity that the material yields in both compression and tension at the same stress magnitude). So what we have in Figure 7.8(c) is a bar in which there is material that is loaded elastically in the centre, with plastically deformed areas at the top and bottom surfaces.

When the load is removed, the material in the elastically deformed zones is constrained from relaxing elastically: the shape of the plastically deformed zone is now different from the central portion of the bar, which has only undergone elastic deformation. This

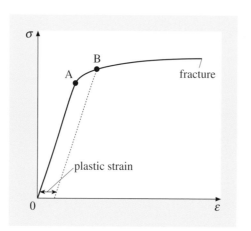

Figure 7.7   Plastic deformation of a tensile test specimen

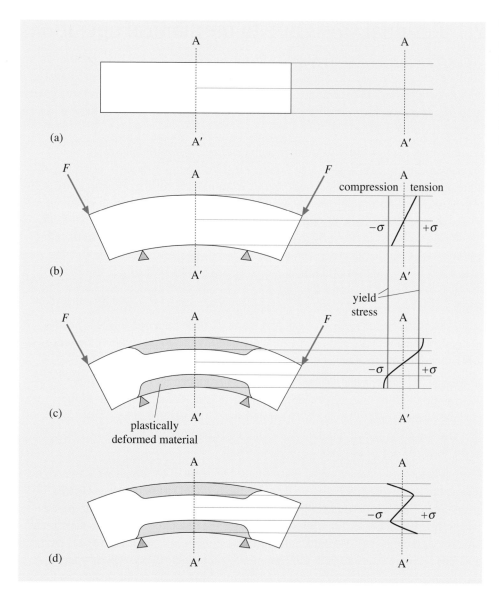

Figure 7.8 Bending of a bar: (a) before bending; (b) initial elastic bending; (c) plasticity occurs when the stress at the surfaces reaches a yield stress; (d) residual stress profile after removal of the load

generates a self-balancing residual stress field, as shown in Figure 7.8(d). One way of conceptualizing this is that the elastic relaxation of the material away from the surfaces 'pulls' the bottom surface into residual tension and 'pushes' the top surface into residual compression. The net effect is the stress profile shown in Figure 7.8(d).

In generating residual stresses, all that changes is the way in which the component is loaded and where the plasticity occurs.

Now that the cause of residual stresses in general has been explained, we will consider how residual stresses are generated (either intentionally or unintentionally) as a result of manufacturing processes. The various manufacturing processes that can result in residual stresses in components can be divided roughly into the following groups:

- Mechanical processes – forming operations, machining, grinding, assembly.

- Thermal processes – heat treatment, welding, casting.

- Chemical processes – such as nitriding and carbonitriding of steels to improve strength.

2.1 Residual stress due to mechanical operations

Practically all mechanical operations (with the exception of assembly operations) produce residual stresses as a result of non-uniform plastic flow. Nearly all metallic components, for example, will go through some sort of mechanical processing as part of their fabrication into something useful, and this means that many of them will end up with residual stresses.

For example, the general method by which residual stresses are produced in a metal-working process is shown in Figure 7.9. This figure represents the rolling of a metal sheet to reduce its thickness. In this example, the rolling conditions are such that plastic flow occurs only near the surfaces of the rolled sheet. As the material passes through the rollers, the surface region of the rolled sheet deforms plastically in the plane parallel to the surface, resulting in elongation and thinning of the plate, while the material in the centre remains elastic. Once the material is through the rollers, the elastic relaxation of the material in the middle of the plate 'pushes' the surface material into compression. The surface layer has elongated plastically, but it is still constrained by the core material. Likewise, the core material cannot relax elastically because it is constrained by the surface material, and so remains in residual tension. This results in a high compressive residual stress at the rolled surface and tensile residual stresses in the mid-thickness of the sheet.

In general, the sign of the residual stress that is produced by heterogeneous deformation will be opposite to the sign of the plastic strain that produced the residual stress. So, for the case of the rolled sheet, the surface material elongated longitudinally by rolling will be left in a state of compressive longitudinal residual stress once the external rolling load is removed.

This situation can be reversed in cases where the depth of plastic deformation is larger. For example, in rod or wire drawing the residual stress profile is largely a function of the depth of penetration of the plastic deformation involved. When penetration is shallow or, in other words, where the reduction in the cross-sectional area for a given pass is small, then the residual stresses are compressive at the surface and tensile in the interior (as in the example of sheet rolling). However, when the penetration is deep, with plasticity occurring through the entire section, as in the case where the reduction in cross-sectional area for a given pass is large, then the resulting residual stress profile is completely reversed: residual stresses are tensile at the surface and balanced by compressive stresses in the interior. This change occurs because, although the whole section becomes plastic as material flows through the

Figure 7.9
(a) Schematic of the deformation in rolled sheet; (b) the resultant through-thickness longitudinal residual-stress profile

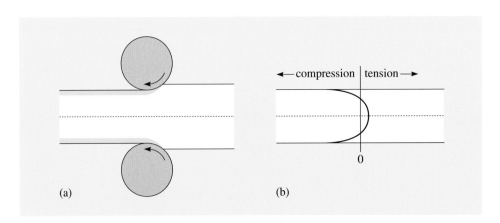

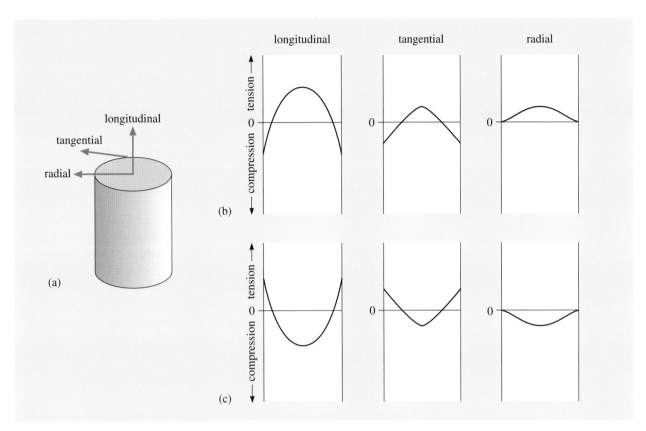

Figure 7.10   (a) Residual stresses produced by wire drawing; (b) and (c) idealized residual stress pattern found in a shallow-drawn and a deep-drawn rod, respectively

die, the plastic deformation is not uniform throughout the thickness: the surface has experienced a greater total strain than the centre, which leaves the centre in residual compression.

The profiles of the residual stress for each stress component within a rod for shallow and deep penetrations are shown in Figure 7.10.

EXERCISE 7.3

A method used in the aerospace industry to improve the integrity of riveted joints is to 'cold expand' the rivet holes. A mandrel, larger than the hole diameter, is pulled through the hole, as shown in Figure 7.11 (often a soft metal sleeve is used to 'lubricate' the passage of the mandrel). The hole is enlarged slightly by the process.

What will be the stress near to the hole in the circumferential, or hoop, direction after the expansion process?

Hint: think about what happens to a small part of the circumference of the hole.

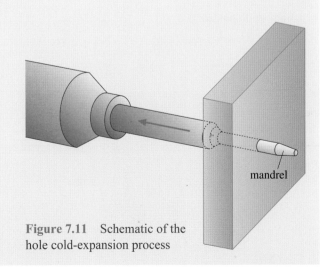

Figure 7.11   Schematic of the hole cold-expansion process

Forming operations such as stamping, coining and bending will produce residual stresses as a result of the non-uniform plastic deformation required to change the shape of the material. Again, as a general rule, regions that are deformed in compression in the plane parallel to the surface will be in residual tension after the external forces have been removed, and vice versa.

However, with forging operations, in which the material is highly plastically deformed to the desired shape using a die, a range of processes takes place. This includes complex deformation fields, thermal gradients and, perhaps, rapid cooling operations. In this case, the relationship of the residual stress distribution to the shape of the part becomes quite complex and cannot be easily predicted.

Stress from surface material removal methods

Many components are subjected to machining operations during their production. This might be a cutting operation to make the desired shape from an initial block or rod, or a final grinding operation to bring a component to within a very tight dimensional specification. Such operations can leave residual stresses in the material due to plastic deformation at the surface associated with the process. If 'good' machining practice or relatively 'gentle' grinding is carried out, then a compressive residual stress field is left at the surface. In fact, virtually all cold, abrasive material-removal processes produce shallow compressive residual stress distributions.

However, with less than gentle grinding, because of a 'dull' (worn) wheel, heavier cuts or inadequate coolant, the surface of the workpiece being ground can see a significant rise in temperature, which may lead to surface tensile residual stress (see Figure 7.12). This is because the yield strength of most materials falls with increasing temperature. Thus, for a given steel, above a critical temperature the surface material

Figure 7.12 Change in residual stress of a typical hardened steel with different grinding conditions. Different stress profiles can be obtained depending on whether 'gentle' or 'abusive' grinding conditions are used

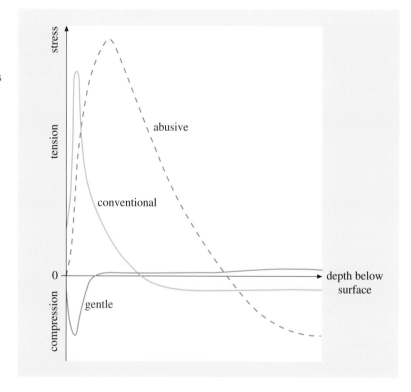

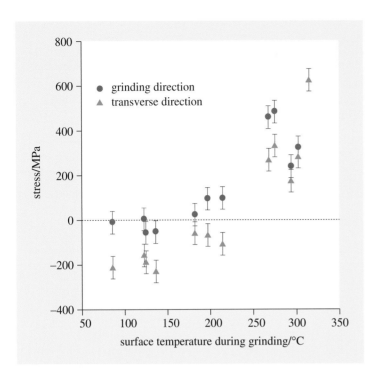

Figure 7.13   Change in residual stress from compression to tension as the surface temperature increases during grinding

will yield in compression from the pressure of the grinding wheel, while the cooler, stronger material below will remain elastic. Upon cooling to room temperature, the surface contracts and is held in residual tension by the undeformed material below. There is usually a critical temperature for the material surface above which tensile stresses, rather than compressive stresses, will be generated (Figure 7.13).

Assembly stresses

Stresses are often developed in the various components of an assembly during manufacture or construction. Whereas individual components can be designed and manufactured with great care in order to minimize the stresses within them, it is important to realize that considerable residual stresses can be generated within these very components when they are joined together, even before any loading is applied to them. This is especially true with large structures such as ships. Often, as the individual components are being joined together by methods such as bolting, welding or riveting, small deviations in the positions of individual components soon add up. Large applied forces, e.g. the use of hydraulic jacks, are then required to correct these alignment errors so that the final pieces can be joined together to create the finished structure. Once the component is finally assembled the applied forces are removed, resulting in large residual stresses being locked into the structure.

Assembly residual stresses become very apparent when the component needs to be dismantled. For example, in a bolted structure the bolts might be difficult to unscrew, and once the bolt was finally removed the ends of the components that were bolted together would spring apart, thereby releasing the locked-in stress.

Figure 7.14 shows a bolted joint, similar to that you saw as part of Exercise 1.4 in Part 1. In that case you calculated the necessary bolt diameter to carry a load of 20 kN.

SAQ 7.1 (Learning outcomes 7.1 and 7.2)

A set of four bolts, each 6 mm in diameter and made of an aluminium alloy with a yield stress of 220 MPa, is used to join two thin metal plates as shown in Figure 7.14. When the plates are subjected to tensile loading, the single shear joint induces shear forces in the bolt cross sections.

(a) Explain why a bolt such as those in Figure 7.14 might carry a residual stress.

(b) Assuming that the applied tensile load of 12 kN in Figure 7.14 is the only significant loading in the joint, show that it is not quite sufficient to cause yielding in the bolts, according to the Tresca yield criterion. (Use a simple plane-stress analysis.)

(c) Imagine that the same 12 kN load is applied to the plates, but that this time the bolts have been tightened so that each experiences a tensile stress of 50 MPa along its length, perpendicular to the plane of the plates. Ignoring friction, will yield now occur?

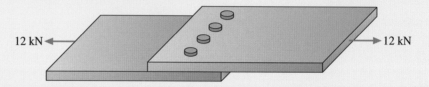

Figure 7.14   Bolted joint

There is an important point to be learned here. One of the critical factors in the design of a component or structure is the stress that it will see while it is being assembled, or even when being transported, if for some reason this leads to higher stresses than during operation. If a material fails during assembly, then that is just as bad as failing under service conditions. But, in addition, the most carefully designed part can be compromised if the assembly methodology and maximum loads are not tightly specified (Figure 7.15).

Figure 7.15   Who determines the final strength of a part?

2.2 Residual stress due to thermal processes

Residual stresses arise from thermal processes if the material being treated experiences a thermal gradient, usually during rapid heating or cooling where different parts of a component may be at different temperatures. Such gradients arise typically during:

- *heat treatment* of alloys to improve their strength, as such processes often involve *quenching* (rapid cooling from a high temperature by plunging into oil or water) to produce a beneficial metallurgical structure or to preserve one that was developed at the higher temperature

- *casting*, where the material close to the mould wall cools faster than the core material

- *welding*, where a pool of molten metal solidifies and cools, surrounded by cooler 'parent' material.

An additional complication can arise during heat treatment of some steels, particularly where changes in the crystal structure of the material cause local volume changes that lead to residual stress generation.

2.2.1 Quenching

Residual stresses from quenching are typically compressive at the component's surface, with balancing tensile stresses in the core.

On quenching, the outer 'shell' of the component will contract faster than the interior, as it is in direct contact with the cold quench medium. The difference in contraction leads to a build-up of stresses between the surface and the interior. Initially, some of the stresses are dissipated by plastic flow in the hot interior, which has a reduced yield stress due to the higher temperature. As the core cools further, its contraction is restrained by the material near the surface, eventually leaving the core in residual tension and the surface in compression.

The quench medium is usually water or oil. However, iced brine may be used to give very rapid cooling, or solutions with a polymer glycol mix can be applied to reduce the cooling rate and so limit the stresses generated.

A classic example of where quenching residual stresses are deliberately engineered is in tempered glass, often used in car windows. In this case, the surface of a hot glass sheet is cooled rapidly by air jets, placing the surface in compression and the interior in tension. The compressive stress at the surface helps to prevent small surface flaws and scratches in the glass from growing. However, if a crack does propagate through beyond the compressive surface layer, then the tensile stresses in the core drive it rapidly through the entire plate, leading to the familiar shatter pattern shown in Figure 7.6. We will look in more detail at the generation of quenching stresses in Section 3, in the context of how residual stresses can be modelled.

2.2.2 Casting

The process of casting can generate residual stresses within the cast component owing to differential contraction within the component during cooling and freezing. Smaller sections of a casting cool and solidify first, leaving larger sections constrained as the metal in those regions contracts as it cools.

2.2.3 Welding

Welding is one of the most significant sources of residual stresses in engineering assemblies, and, as most large structures (from buildings to ships and aircraft) are at least partly welded, being able to understand and quantify the effect of these residual stresses is extremely important. A feature of welding processes is that the magnitude of the residual stresses generated can be close to (and in some cases even above) the yield stress of the material.

Residual stresses are generated whenever welding is carried out. This is because the weld, as the metal cools and solidifies, contracts more than the adjacent metal, which has not been subjected to the same high temperature. This extra thermal contraction of the weld imposes strains on the surrounding material, resulting in the generation of residual stresses.

> ## SAQ 7.2 (Learning outcome 7.1)
>
> From the simple description of welding you have just read, suggest what type of residual stresses you might expect to find in a weld after solidification:
>
> (a) in the material that has been melted and resolidified
>
> (b) in the surrounding material.

For a more detailed explanation of the generation of stress in welded material, have a look at ☑ **The three-bar model of weld residual stress** ☑.

☑ The three-bar model of weld residual stress

The 'three-bar model' is a simple way of visualizing the generation of residual stress in a welded joint; see Figure 7.16. The weld fusion zone corresponds to the central hot bar, which is flanked by two cold bars representing the material around the weld location. The bars, initially of the same length, are regarded as being fixed together by rigid end pieces; in other words, the bars must all remain the same length because the fusion zone remains the same length as the adjoining material to which it is attached.

Figure 7.16
(a) 'Three-bar model';
(b) change in length of the bars

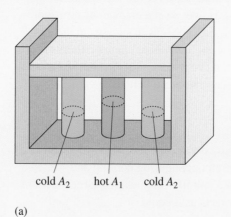

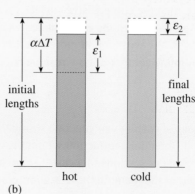

(a)

(b)

When the weld is still liquid the central bar is stress free, but stresses build up as the weld pool cools, solidifies and contracts.

We'll assume our bars have a thermal expansion coefficient α and a starting length of 1 m (so we don't have to keep putting an unknown length l into our calculations). Take the central bar first. If it has a cross-sectional area A_1 and cools through a temperature range ΔT, then it will undergo a thermal contraction of $\alpha \Delta T$. It will also experience an elastic strain ε_1 in order to maintain the same length as the outer bars (see Figure 7.16b). The two outer bars are taken to have identical cross-sectional areas A_2, and undergo an elastic strain ε_2. Now we can put together the following relations to quantify the stresses generated in the three-bar system.

The *total* length change in the inner bar must be equal to that in the outer bars:

$$\alpha \Delta T + \varepsilon_1 = \varepsilon_2 \qquad (7.1)$$

Since any forces generated here are uniaxial, we can use Hooke's law in the form $\sigma = E\varepsilon$, so that this expression can be rewritten as follows:

$$\alpha \Delta T + \frac{\sigma_1}{E} = \frac{\sigma_2}{E} \qquad (7.2)$$

where σ_1 and σ_2 are the stresses in the inner and outer bars respectively. Equation (7.2) can be rearranged to produce:

$$E\alpha \Delta T = \sigma_2 - \sigma_1 \qquad (7.3)$$

The force $\sigma_1 A_1$ exerted by the inner bar on the outer bars must be equal and opposite to $2\sigma_2 A_2$, as there are no external forces acting on the system. So:

$$\sigma_1 A_1 = -2\sigma_2 A_2 \qquad (7.4)$$

Equations (7.3) and (7.4) can now be solved for the residual stresses σ_1 and σ_2 in the bars.

EXAMPLE

If we take the following values for steel:

$$\Delta T = -200 \text{ K}; \alpha = 12 \times 10^{-6} \text{ K}^{-1}; A_1 = A_2;$$
$$E = 200 \text{ GPa}$$

what are the values of residual stress in the fusion zone according to this model?

SOLUTION

Using Equation (7.3) we have:

$$\sigma_2 - \sigma_1 = 200 \times 10^9 \text{ Pa} \times 12 \times 10^{-6} \text{ K}^{-1} \times -200$$

$$\sigma_2 - \sigma_1 = -480 \times 10^6 \text{ Pa} \qquad (7.5)$$

As $A_1 = A_2$, Equation (7.4) gives:

$$\sigma_1 = -2\sigma_2 \qquad (7.6)$$

Substituting for σ_1 in Equation (6.5) gives:

$$\sigma_2 = -160 \text{MPa}$$

thus

$$\sigma_1 = 320 \text{MPa}$$

The residual tensile stress of 320 MPa in the central bar is of the order of the room-temperature yield strength for many steels, and can be generated if the weld cools by only 200 K more than the adjacent weld metal.

In practice, welds can cool by much more than this, but the residual stress cannot rise too far above the yield stress because, at such stresses, the weld metal would accommodate the strain by plastic deformation – or by cracking when severe residual stresses are generated very quickly.

Figure 7.17(a) shows the residual profile across the three-bar model. In a real welded joint, of course, instead of the uniform residual stresses in the three-bar model, the residual stresses parallel to a welded joint will vary smoothly across the weld (Figure 7.17b).

More complicated stress profiles can be obtained (see Figure 7.18), for example, in complex alloy systems that can be both softened and hardened by the welding heat profile, depending on exactly how fast they are heated and cooled and to what temperature.

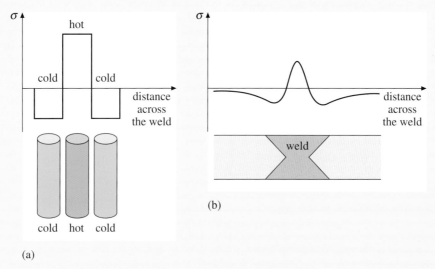

Figure 7.17   (a) The distribution of residual stress in the three-bar model; (b) the distribution of residual stress in a typical welded joint

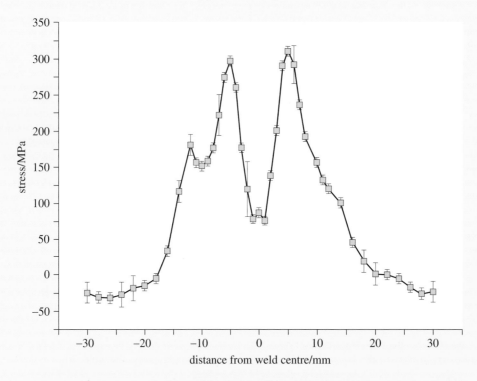

Figure 7.18   Residual stress in a welded aluminium plate. Although the overall pattern is tensile in the weld and compressive in the parent plate, the stress oscillates because of changes in the properties of the material during heating and cooling

Weld residual stresses are of particular cause for concern in thick, welded components, where the wall thickness being welded may be greater than 25 mm; such thick sections are typically found in pressure vessels, the cooling circuits of power plants and other industrial pipework. Thick sections provide a large amount of constraint for the weld, which can lead to a residual triaxial stress of considerable magnitude. If a triaxial stress field exists that is tensile in all directions, then it can promote the growth of cracks and can cause a usually ductile material to fail in a brittle manner.

Conversely, in thinner components, instead of large residual stresses being generated, considerable distortion of a component can occur. This in itself is a significant problem where tight dimensional tolerances are required.

2.3 Residual stress due to chemical processes

Residual stresses due to chemical processes can include those from chemical surface-hardening treatments and those from oxidation or corrosion processes.

Surface-hardening treatments are commonly applied to steel components by exposing the surface to nitrogen, *nitriding*, or carbon, *carburizing*, at elevated temperatures. The aim of these treatments is to diffuse the nitrogen or carbon atoms into the surface layer of the component, where they cause a large increase in hardness. Such hardening treatments essentially cause a volume expansion within the region where carbon or nitrogen atoms have penetrated into the material; the diffusing atoms strain the atomic structure in such a way as to produce compressive stresses at the surface of the component. The depth of this diffusion zone, and so the depth of the final residual stress field, will depend on the temperature of the component, the concentration of nitrogen or carbon adjacent to the component surface, and the length of time of exposure.

Not as well known is the fact that oxidation and corrosion processes are also sources of residual stresses. In fact, large stresses may be generated by the formation of an oxide scale or other reaction product on the surface of the metal during oxidation or corrosion. In oxidation, stresses arise because the oxide usually occupies a larger volume than the metal from which it was formed.

SAQ 7.3 (Learning outcome 7.1)

If an oxide forms on a metal surface and it has a larger volume than the metal, suggest what the residual stresses will be in the oxide if:

(a) the oxide remains firmly adhered to the metal

(b) the oxide spalls off in small flakes.

The constraint on the expansion of the oxide layer results in it being placed in compression by the bulk metal; the latter therefore must be in tension to maintain equilibrium. These stresses can play a major role in oxidation processes by influencing spalling, warping and even the dimensional stability of the metal.

2.4 Controlling residual stress

Once a component has a residual stress within it, are we stuck with it permanently? The answer is no. However, removing a residual stress is often non-trivial and may actually make things worse.

When stresses are produced in simple products, such as sheet, plate and extrusions, they can be removed by stretching the material beyond the yield stress: this relieves the residual stress by uniform plastic deformation. This can change the strength and toughness properties of the material; but for steel products that have large ductilities, the benefits of removing the residual stress can far outweigh any drawbacks.

One of the most common methods of relieving residual stresses in metals is by exposing the component to elevated temperatures. The temperature the component is treated at depends on the melting point of the metal. From a metallurgical point of view, residual stresses are relaxed by a process called *creep*, the rate of which is strongly dependent on temperature. To compare different metals, it is useful to express temperature on a homologous scale T_H, in which it is normalized with respect to the melting temperature T_m of the metal:

$$T_H = T/T_m$$

where T is the treatment temperature; all temperatures are in kelvin. Creep generally becomes significant at temperatures above $0.4T_m$, but for residual stresses to be relieved quickly the temperature at which stress relief occurs is typically closer to $0.8T_m$.

EXERCISE 7.4

Stainless steel has a melting point of 1400 °C. At what temperature would a stainless steel component need to be treated for a stress-relief treatment at $0.8T_m$?

In fact, a typical stress-relief process for stainless steel would be 1050 °C for 30 min.

However, in order to design a stress-relief treatment for a given material, it is important that the metallurgical structure of the material is not altered. For example, some of the commonly used aluminium alloys in aircraft structures rely on an even distribution of hard precipitates in order to achieve maximum strength; these precipitates are produced in the material by a tightly controlled heat-treatment process. Consequently, by increasing the temperature in such a material it is possible to 'over age' the material, i.e. the precipitates grow too large to be effective or, even worse, they redissolve into the material. This would result in a much softer material, making it no longer fit for purpose.

Other difficulties involve the practical considerations of thermally treating large welded pipelines. In such cases, a localized input of heat can be used to relieve stresses in only part of a much larger structure. However, such processes may be possible only if the part can be easily accessed, and where the thermal conductivity of the material is sufficiently low in order to allow localized heating without having to heat up the entire structure, which may be hundreds of kilometres long!

Another strategy is to limit the formation of stresses where possible. In the case of welding, this may be possible by preheating a component before welding. In this way, the difference in temperature between the weld metal and the parent metal is reduced, thus decreasing the magnitude of thermal stresses generated.

3 ANALYSIS OF RESIDUAL STRESS: MODELLING

The measurement and prediction of residual stresses is generally difficult and, hence, expensive to perform. Therefore, in cases where the level of residual stresses within a given structure is expected to be low, or in components where safety is not critical – i.e. where failure of the component will not lead to catastrophic consequences – or in cases where, historically, components have been designed and operated satisfactorily with no consideration of residual stress, these stresses are largely ignored. However, where a component's safety may depend on the presence or otherwise of residual stress, its presence must be included in calculations.

Unfortunately, if it is known that a residual stress may be present (e.g. because the component in question has been welded) but the size and distribution of the residual stress field is unknown, then it may be that a worst-case approximation will have to be made for some calculations, i.e. that everywhere the residual stress is close to the yield stress. Of course, this can then lead to highly overconservative design. It would be far better if the magnitude and evolution of residual stresses within the component were properly understood. This would include the generation of residual stresses during manufacture and, in the case where the initial residual stress state is known, the effect of these initial residual stresses on a given component during its operational lifetime.

In applications where the residual stresses within a component have been judged to be of concern, an engineer can either attempt to predict the magnitude and spatial distribution of residual stresses within the component or attempt to determine the residual stresses within an existing component through carrying out measurements. This section deals with the modelling of residual stresses and is followed by a discussion of measurement techniques in Section 4.

A highly desirable goal for any engineer is to be able to model accurately a manufacturing process, or the lifetime operating conditions of a product, from beginning to end and be able to predict the evolution of residual stresses at each stage. With such information the engineer could then make adjustments to a given process to minimize or, where residual stresses are desirable, maximize the residual stresses. Unfortunately, in practice such models are seldom, if ever, available.

Residual stresses are commonly predicted by the use of finite element models. You have already seen how such models can be used to predict the strains and stresses within a component as a result of applied loading. The modelling of residual stresses is more complex as it requires an understanding of plastic deformation. The plastic behaviour of metals is not as straightforward to characterize as their elastic behaviour, particularly if one needs to understand how the plastic behaviour is affected by changes in temperature for heat treatment or welding processes.

In terms of the characterization of a material for the modelling of residual stress, knowledge will be required of the following:

- At what point does the material start to deform plastically (i.e. what is its yield stress)?

- Is this yield stress the same in tension as in compression? We have made this simplifying assumption in general throughout this block, but the tensile and compressive yield stresses often differ, particularly as a function of:

    how the material hardens during plastic deformation (see ☑ **Isotropic and kinematic hardening** ☑), and

    how the plasticity and hardening properties vary at different temperatures.

☑ Isotropic and kinematic hardening

You have seen previously (Part 2, Section 5) that materials can exhibit different behaviours following yield, i.e. in terms of being ductile or brittle. However, the way that materials deform plastically affects the magnitude of the residual stresses that will be generated within them. This is particularly the case where a material will have yielded in both tension and compression during a process.

We have usually made the assumption in this course that metallic materials have the same yield strengths in both tension and compression. In general, that is true; but once a material has been deformed plastically its yield strength may change. This may simply be a consequence of work hardening (as shown in Figure 7.19), where the yield strength has increased as a result of plastic deformation. However, yielding a material in tension may affect the compressive yield stress in different ways.

When a material is work-hardened in tension, so increasing its yield stress, the compressive yield stress may increase, i.e. a larger magnitude of compressive stress is needed to cause yield by the same amount. This is known as *isotropic hardening*.

At the other extreme, increasing the tensile yield stress may *decrease* the compressive yield stress by an equivalent amount. This is known as *kinematic hardening*. These extremes are shown schematically in Figure 7.19.

In practice, the behaviour of real materials tends to fall somewhere in between, and the compressive yield stress could remain unchanged; so often a 'mixed' approach is used so that the model reflects the actual material behaviour fairly accurately.

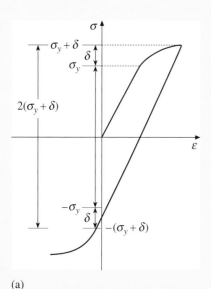

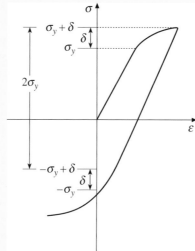

(a)   (b)

Figure 7.19
(a) Isotropic and (b) kinematic hardening

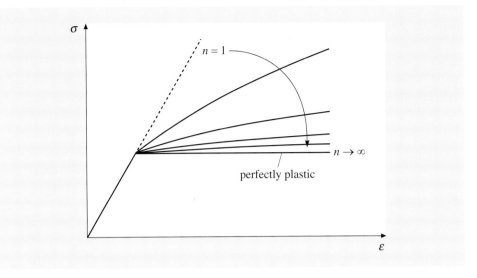

Figure 7.20   Schematic stress–strain curves showing different hardening behaviours

Such materials information is commonly determined from a uniaxial tensile test or a series of such tests performed at different temperatures. You should already be familiar with using such tests for the determination of elastic modulus and yield or proof stress. However, for the accurate determination of residual stresses, knowledge of precisely how the material behaves once plastic deformation begins is needed. Figure 7.20 shows a series of schematic stress–strain curves, with different behaviours following yield. The material may behave *perfectly plastically* following yield, which means that once the yield stress is reached there is no further increase in stress and the material just elongates to its failure strain. Or, as is the case with most metals, it will 'work harden', where an increase in stress is needed to strain the material further, although the elongation for a given stress increase is greater than when the material is deforming elastically. A figure known as the ☑ **strain-hardening exponent** ☑ is used to describe mathematically the hardening behaviour after yield.

Measurement of elastic modulus and proof stress is covered in the 'Testing of materials and structures' programme on the course DVD.

☑ Strain-hardening exponent

Finite element models need to have mathematical descriptions of materials' behaviour. For the different work-hardening behaviours shown in Figure 7.20, an equation for describing the strain as a function of stress is used:

$$\varepsilon = \frac{\sigma_{\text{yield}}}{E} + \alpha\sigma^n$$

where α is the strain-hardening coefficient and n is the strain-hardening exponent n, which is dimensionless, varies from infinity for perfectly plastic materials to unity for materials that are essentially only elastic. In practice, values of n for most materials range between about 3 and 20.

Once a finite element mesh has been generated, and the elastic and plastic behaviour defined within the model, then only the loading by which the plastic strain is caused needs to be determined. In the case of bending a beam, only the position and magnitude of the applied forces need to be defined, which are then the boundary conditions on the finite element model. However, for simulations of more complex problems many other factors need to be incorporated into the model. In the case of a rolling simulation this may require information on friction between the rollers and the material, and if higher temperatures are envisaged, then heat losses through convection (into the air) and conduction (loss of heat from the sheet into the contacting rollers) will be required, not to mention material properties at a range of different temperatures.

EXERCISE 7.5

Suggest five parameters that would have to be included when building a finite element model of the residual stress generated when a steel plate is quenched from 850 °C into oil at room temperature.

SAQ 7.4 (Learning outcome 7.3)

As mentioned earlier, residual stresses arising from welding are often of concern for engineers; however, simulation of such residual stresses poses one of the greatest challenges for modellers. Suggest five parameters that would have to be included when building a finite element model of a weld process in order to calculate the residual stress from welding.

Let's look at an example of developing a finite element model for residual stress generation, in ▽ **Finite element modelling of quenching stresses** ▽.

▽ Finite element modelling of quenching stresses

The material properties of metal alloys are often optimized using a series of heat treatments in which the alloy is raised to a uniform temperature, held for a period of time, and then cooled back to room temperature. Such processing helps to refine the microstructure of the alloy, e.g. the size, shape and nature of the different strengthening phases, so that a component has material properties that are most suitable for its intended use. Appropriate heat-treatment cycles can be chosen to make an alloy harder and more brittle, or softer and more ductile, depending on its susceptibility to in-service fracture or yield.

A crucial part of any heat-treatment cycle is the cooling rate. High cooling rates, often achieved by rapidly quenching the metal in oil or water, are useful in obtaining beneficial properties, particularly strength, but are often accompanied by unacceptably high internal residual stresses. In a finished component these can cause problematic distortions in component dimensions. Furthermore, any subsequent machining is hampered by the elastic relaxation of these stresses as material is removed, causing further distortion.

To illustrate how quenching residual stresses evolve, let us look at a finite element model of a simple nickel superalloy component that is cooled in oil. Nickel superalloys are 'high-temperature' engineering alloys, designed specifically for use at high stresses in the hot, corrosive environment of modern gas-turbine engines. These alloys often ▷

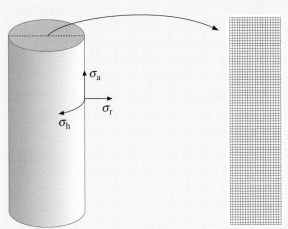

Figure 7.21 In an axisymmetric finite element simulation the stress state in all radial planes is assumed to be the same, and can be characterized by three components σ_a, σ_h and σ_r, in the axial, hoop and radial directions respectively

3D cylindrical geometry   2D finite element mesh of radial plane

undergo quenching to 'freeze in' the desirable microstructure that forms during solution heat treatment. This process is designed to encourage optimum precipitation of certain hardening phases.

The finite element simulation examines a simple cylindrical bar, 20 mm in diameter and 80 mm long, made from nickel superalloy IN718, a material widely used to make aeroengine turbine discs. Because a cylinder is symmetrical about its axis, the finite element simulation can make a two-dimensional approximation of the three-dimensional geometry by assuming *axisymmetry*. This is illustrated in Figure 7.21, where the two-dimensional finite element mesh represents *any* radial plane through the cylinder.

For cylindrical shapes it is usual to consider three directions related to the geometry: axial (along the

cylinder axis), radial (in the direction of any radius) and hoop (around the cylinder). The finite element mesh can be used to present any of these stress components in the two-dimensional radial plane.

In this particular finite element simulation, the bar is initially held in a furnace at a uniform temperature of 1000 °C and then suddenly plunged into a large bath of oil at a temperature of 25 °C. Heat is transferred quickly out of the bar and into the oil; the rate at which this happens depends on the rate at which heat can be carried across the interface between the alloy and the oil, as well as on their thermal properties. Heat is lost from the outside of the bar first, so the surface cools most rapidly, and the centre of the bar stays hot for the longest time. This is illustrated in Figure 7.22, which shows the

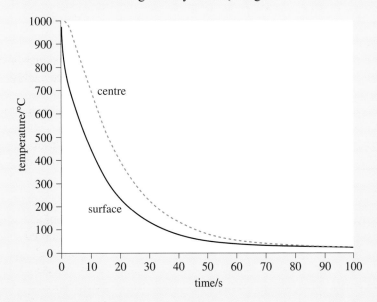

Figure 7.22 Predicted temperature evolution at bar mid-length after quenching in oil

predicted temperature change at the centre and at the surface of the bar (both measured at the bar mid-length).

Note that the bar cools from 1000 °C to room temperature in about 100 s, with the temperature difference between the inner and outer regions reaching around 200 °C when cooling is most rapid. It is this temperature gradient, and the associated differences in mechanical behaviour, that set up the final residual stress state.

Before we try to understand how the residual stresses actually arise, it is worth pointing out the variety of data that must be supplied to the finite element software in order for it to make a reliable prediction. For this particular model the key material properties required for nickel superalloy IN718 were:

- elastic properties (Young's modulus and Poisson's ratio)

- yield stress

- post-yield hardening behaviour (how the load-bearing ability of the alloy increases after yield)

- coefficient of thermal expansion

- thermal conductivity (how easily heat flows through the alloy)

- specific heat capacity (the ability of the alloy to store heat)

- emissivity of the alloy surface (how effectively the surface of the alloy radiates heat)

- heat transfer coefficient (how easily heat is conducted across the alloy–oil interface).

Furthermore, the *temperature dependence* of all these properties needs to be known over the entire range of the heat treatment cycle, 25–1000 °C. Acquiring these data is non-trivial, and the quality of information used will have a significant bearing on the confidence with which the final analysis can be interpreted.

Let us return to looking at the residual stress state in the bar as it is cooled. To illustrate what happens, I will concentrate on the evolution of the *axial stress*, since this turns out to be the dominant stress component in the bar. Figure 7.23 shows how the mid-length axial stress evolves at points on the surface and at the centre of the bar, i.e. the same positions at which the temperature evolution was considered in Figure 7.22. Initially, the stress state is dictated by elastic, thermal contraction of the material. During the first few seconds after quenching, the surface of the bar experiences a faster cooling rate than the centre; this means that the outside of the bar contracts more than the centre, effectively squeezing the inside and placing the centre of the bar in compression. To maintain equilibrium, the near-surface material experiences a balancing tensile stress; compare the surface and

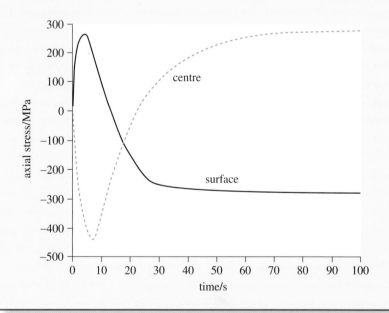

Figure 7.23   Predicted axial stress evolution at the bar mid-length after quenching in oil

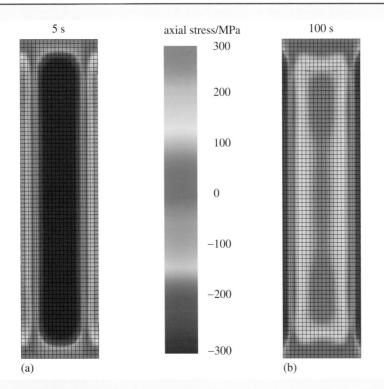

5 s   axial stress/MPa   100 s

Figure 7.24 Axial stress predicted across a radial plane in the quenched bar after (a) 5 s and (b) 100 s

(a)   (b)

centre stresses after 5 s in Figure 7.23. The overall axial stress state in the bar after 5 s is shown in Figure 7.24(a); the outer tension is balanced by inner compression across the whole component. Note that these tensile and compressive elastic stresses do not keep rising continuously, but are eventually limited by yielding, leading to the stress peaks in Figure 7.23.

If you examine Figure 7.22 carefully you will see that, after about 10 s, the cooling rate at the centre of the bar becomes more rapid than at the surface, with the consequence that the centre wants to contract more quickly than the outside. The result is that further contraction of the bar interior is resisted by the exterior, and hence the centre starts to experience a tensile stress. Again, equilibrium tells us that the stress in the outer regions must simultaneously become more compressive, and Figure 7.23 shows that the signs of the axial stresses at the surface and centre of the bar reverse. A final residual stress state of outer compression and inner tension is reached; see Figure 7.24(b).

I've concentrated on the axial stress component, but, so that you can get an idea of the complex nature of the stress state that arises, take a look at Figure 7.25. Here, I have plotted all three final residual stress components (in the axial, hoop and radial directions) along a line across the bar mid-length. You can see that the axial stress σ_a displays the largest variation, which is why I chose to look at it. The hoop stress σ_h does not attain such a high magnitude in tension, while the radial stress σ_r remains relatively small and tensile across the width of the bar. Nevertheless, all three components show the same overall trend: they become more compressive near the surface of the rod, and more tensile near its centre.

Note that significant residual stresses occur only because of non-uniform yielding across the component brought about by the existence of thermal gradients; had only elastic deformation occurred, then no residual stresses would have been generated as a result of this heat treatment. In other words, if the thermal gradients are very small then the residual stresses can become negligible. For example, when I reran the above finite element model using exactly the same parameters as above, except that I allowed cooling to occur slowly (in air) over a period of 500 s, the largest residual stress anywhere in the bar was less than 10 MPa.

Finally, this stress-reversal behaviour and the final residual stress state of outer compression and inner tension are typical of many cylindrical and

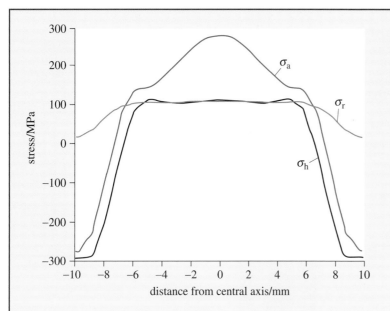

Figure 7.25   Residual axial, hoop and radial stresses along a line across the bar mid-length after cooling

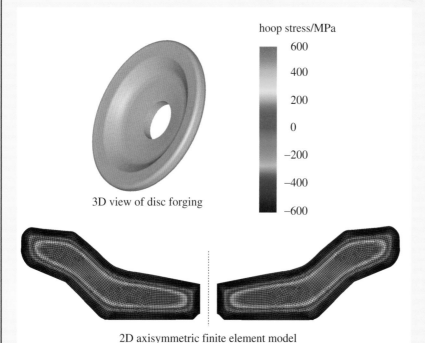

Figure 7.26   Quenching residual stresses (hoop component) in a forged and heat-treated turbine disc, diameter 400 mm

disc geometries. Figure 7.26 shows the predicted residual stress state in a large, 400 mm diameter, aeroengine turbine disc, made of superalloy IN718, after quenching in water. The alloy material properties used in this model were exactly the same as those for the small bar detailed above. Only the heat-transfer properties were altered to take account of the nature of the quenchant. Note that in Figure 7.26 I have plotted the hoop stress component, which was the largest stress component for this geometry. For disc shapes, the axial dimension is a lot smaller than for long rods; hence, axial stresses are also much smaller. Note the large magnitude of the stresses (water is a very effective quenchant and gives rise to high thermal gradients) and the characteristic outer compression and inner tension.

The challenges faced by a computer modeller are considerable when trying to calculate residual stress. For this reason it is often essential that finite element simulations are well validated by measurements on components that have undergone the same process as that simulated in the finite element model. This is particularly the case where the measurements are used to make calculations on safety-critical components, such as in power plant and aerospace applications. The next section introduces the various tools available for residual stress measurements.

4 ANALYSIS OF RESIDUAL STRESS: MEASUREMENT

In Block 1 Part 2 you were introduced to methods of experimental stress analysis in materials, in particular the strain gauge and photoelastic techniques. Such methods are useless when trying to determine the residual stress in a material: they show a response when a load is applied to a component, but they can't reveal the presence of locked-in residual stress, particularly if the peak stress is some way below the surface of the component.

Nevertheless, as residual stresses are often more difficult to predict than the in-service stresses on which they superimpose, it is important to have reliable methods to determine these stresses.

Although the title of this section is 'measurement' of residual stress, in practice stress can rarely be measured directly. What is usually measured is strain; stress is then calculated using the conversion equations from Part 2.

The methods of residual stress measurement are generally divided into two main categories: destructive and non-destructive. Put simply, this classification tells you whether or not the component of interest is still usable after the measurements have been performed!

4.1 Destructive residual stress measurement methods

The unintentional relaxation of residual stress during cutting can be a problem in some industrial processing. If a sample containing a high residual stress is machined, it can move and distort so that the cut is not straight, the final dimensions are incorrect, or the cut faces close up and break the cutting tool. However, the tendency of residual stress to cause a measurable strain in a sample when the stress is relaxed offers a useful method of determining it.

Destructive stress-measurement methods generally involve removing material from a sample in some way. This is done to cause at least partial relaxation of the residual stress field within the sample, whilst the resulting strain is measured. The residual stress that caused the deformation can then be calculated from measurements of the deformation response.

4.1.1 Hole drilling

Perhaps the most common method of residual stress measurement is the hole-drilling method. A strain-gauge rosette, containing three strain gauges as shown in Figure 7.27, is attached to the sample and a hole is drilled in the centre of the rosette.

Historically, the hole-drilling method was used for fairly simple stress measurement, in situations where the stress close to the surface was needed and where the in-plane stress distribution did not vary greatly with depth. The measured strains from the

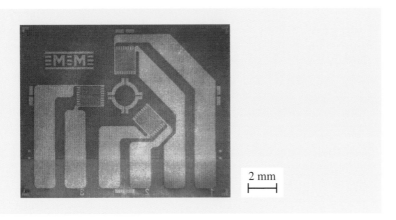

Figure 7.27 A strain-gauge rosette used for the hole-drilling method

gauges around the hole could be used to calculate an average of the in-plane principal stresses over the depth of the hole.

More sophisticated analytical methods have evolved for using the data from the strain-gauge rosette as a hole is drilled *incrementally* into a sample, taking strain readings at successive depth increments to obtain a profile of the near-surface stresses. The analysis methods used, which rely on finite element models and calibration functions – obtained from drilling holes into (real or modelled) samples with known applied stresses and observing the resulting strains – are quite sophisticated, so there is no easy way of performing the calculations.

The drilling method can provide information on the principal stress in the plane of the sample at depths of up to several millimetres. The diameter of the drill bit needs to be selected carefully, as it is found that the strain gauges are insensitive to stresses at depths greater than 1.2 times the hole diameter beneath the sample surface.

4.1.2 The contour method

The contour method is a relatively new method for stress measurement, but it has significant advantages over many other conventional techniques. The method is illustrated in Figure 7.28. A component containing a residual stress field is cut in two (Figure 7.28a). The cut needs to be made in such a way that it does not introduce any 'new' stresses into the component. In practice, this means that an accurate cutting method such as ▽ **electro-discharge machining** ▽ must be used, and that the specimen must be clamped during cutting so that there is no change in the residual stress field from distortion during cutting. Any residual stresses that were acting across the cut plane (normal to the cut) must be relaxed when the cutting occurs, as there can be no stress normal to a free surface, even for residual stresses – surfaces, remember, are always in a condition of plane stress. So the contour profile on the surface of each half is indicative of the residual stress that existed previously normal to the newly cut surface, as shown in Figure 7.28(b). This contour profile can be measured accurately with micrometre resolution, using a standard method, such as a coordinate measuring machine (Figure 7.29).

DVD

The hole-drilling method is described in the 'Hole-drilling residual stress analysis' programme on the course DVD.

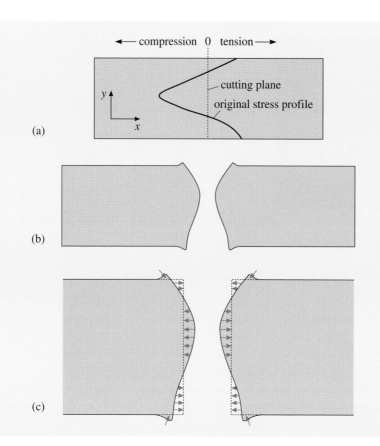

(a)

(b)

(c)

Figure 7.28 Schematic of the contour method: (a) a sample containing a residual stress field is cut in half; (b) the cutting relaxes the stress field normal to the cut, producing a distortion of the cut surface, and the resulting surface contour is measured; (c) a finite element model is used to calculate the stress needed to 'force' the contour back to a flat surface

☑ Electro-discharge machining

Electro-discharge machining (EDM) is a highly accurate method for the machining of metallic materials. The method works by immersing the workpiece to be cut in a conducting fluid. The cut is made with a wire held at a high voltage relative to the workpiece. When the wire is brought close to the workpiece, the high voltage causes sparks to arc between the wire and the workpiece; the local heating caused by the spark causes local melting, which gradually erodes the workpiece, so the wire effectively cuts through it. The wire is usually fed slowly between two spools to prevent it from breaking due to self-erosion, and the fluid is circulated to remove debris. EDM is often used where accurate dimensioning or surface finishing is needed.   △

The free-surface profile that has been measured is then 'forced' back virtually to its original flat profile using a finite element model (Figure 7.28c). It is not possible to obtain the entire stress field that existed in the part before cutting; but, as stresses normal to the free surface must be zero, the correct σ_x stress field originally present can be calculated. Both of the cut surfaces need to be measured, or errors can be introduced because of shear stresses.

The contour method has the advantage that, unlike hole drilling and other sectioning methods, it can map large cross-sectional areas with a single cut. However, it is a relatively new method and, thus, lacks the standardized practical and analytical tools of more mature techniques. Therefore, it is fairly expensive owing to the need for a person to work on the data analysis and development of the finite element model. An example of a result from the contour method is shown in Figure 7.30.

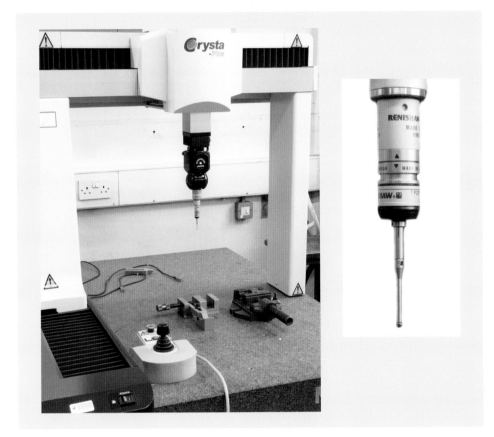

Figure 7.29
A coordinate measuring machine, which uses a contact probe to determine a surface profile accurately

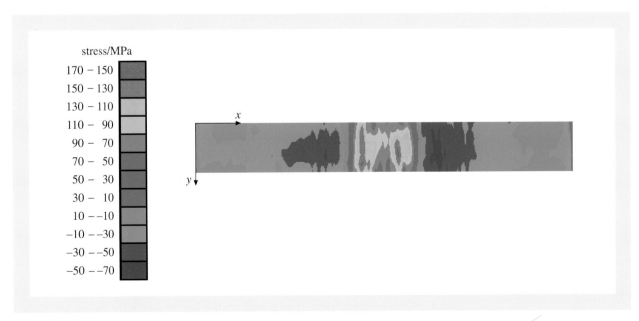

stress/MPa

170 − 150	
150 − 130	
130 − 110	
110 − 90	
90 − 70	
70 − 50	
50 − 30	
30 − 10	
10 − −10	
−10 − −30	
−30 − −50	
−50 − −70	

Figure 7.30   The stress field on the cross section of a welded plate, measured using the contour method

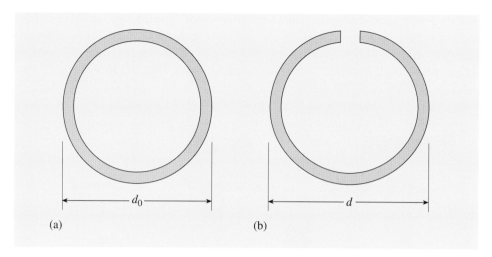

Figure 7.31   The tube-splitting method: (a) before cutting; (b) after longitudinal cut

4.1.3 Other sectioning and layer-removal methods

Other sectioning and layer-removal techniques exist that are conceptually the same as the hole-drilling and contour methods. They involve the removal of part of a sample either by mechanical cutting or chemical etching while measuring the deformation response of the remaining sample, often by means of strain gauges. Some of these methods are conceptually simple, such as *tube splitting*, where a tube containing a residual stress is slit longitudinally and the movement of the tube is used to infer the hoop residual stress that was present (Figure 7.31).

More complex methods involve multiple machining operations, such as deep-hole drilling. In this method a hole is drilled, up to 450 mm deep, and its internal surface is accurately profiled. The change in this profile is then measured as a cylinder containing the original hole is extracted from the sample. The changes measured can be used to calculate the original stresses.

4.2 Non-destructive residual stress measurement methods

As the name implies, these methods use some form of probe, such as X-rays, sound waves or magnetism, to determine the residual stress without damaging the component being measured. In principle, the component can be reused or tested further without the measuring method having changed its properties or performance.

4.2.1 Diffraction methods

The measurement of residual stress using diffraction is based on the principle that the crystalline lattice can be used like an 'atomic strain gauge'. A conventional strain gauge works by measuring deformations of the surface to which it is affixed. Diffraction methods measure deformations of the atomic lattice of a crystalline material, which in practice means that they can be applied to most metals and ceramics. Stresses change the atomic spacing – not by much, but enough to cause a measurable change. As you might expect, a tensile stress pulls the atoms further apart, in the direction of the applied stress, and a compressive stress pushes them closer together.

For stress measurement, some form of radiation needs to be used that will penetrate into a solid material. In practice, X-rays are commonly used for near-surface stresses, as a standard laboratory machine will produce X-rays that will penetrate to a depth of around 50 μm. (It is possible to combine the laboratory X-ray method with layer removal to measure stresses several millimetres below a surface, but then of course the method is no longer non-destructive.)

More specialized techniques, requiring dedicated large-scale national or international facilities, and using high-energy X-rays or neutrons, can penetrate 50 mm or even further, allowing stress measurement deep inside bulk components.

Diffraction itself is a phenomenon that occurs wherever a travelling wave is incident on a set of regularly spaced scattering objects, provided that the wavelength of the incoming wave is of the same order of magnitude as the repeat distance between the scattering centres. In the case of crystalline materials the spacing of the atoms (the scattering centres) is of the same order of magnitude (a few angstroms) as the wavelength of neutrons and X-rays.

> An angstrom (Å) is equal to 0.1 nm or 10^{-10} m. Although non SI, it is a fairly standard measurement unit when dealing with crystal structures.

Diffraction from crystals follows Bragg's law. If radiation with a wavelength λ is incident on a crystal and is diffracted from lattice planes of spacing d, diffraction peaks will be observed at an angle 2θ relative to the incident beam (Figure 7.32).

This is described mathematically as:

$$\lambda = 2d \sin\theta$$

so an increase in the lattice spacing d causes the diffraction angle to be reduced, and vice versa. So, for increasing tensile stress a decrease in diffraction angle will be observed (Figure 7.32b).

As with the destructive methods, what is actually measured is strain, from which stress is then calculated. The geometry of the measurement provides information about the strain component that is being measured (Figure 7.32a). In order to obtain a stress component, several strains will be measured by changing the orientation of the sample relative to the incident and diffracted beams. It is the direction that bisects the incident and diffracted beams that is the measured strain direction, as shown in Figure 7.32.

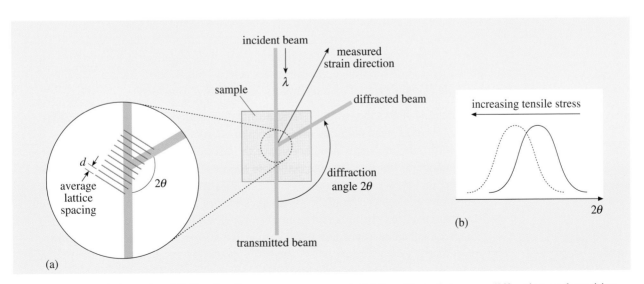

Figure 7.32   (a) Schematic of diffraction for stress measurement; (b) the effect of stress on diffraction peak position

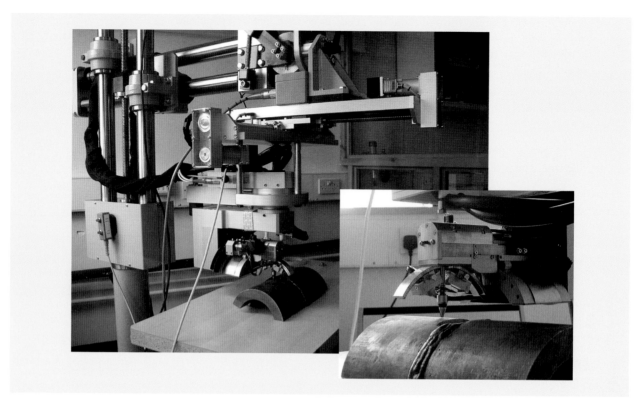

Figure 7.33   Sample being measured on a laboratory X-ray diffractometer

Strain is calculated from the change in lattice spacing, which gives, from Bragg's law:

$$\varepsilon = \frac{d - d_0}{d_0} = -\frac{\Delta\theta}{\tan\theta_0}$$

where d_0 and the associated θ_0 are the values of d and θ for the material in an *unstressed* condition. Several methods are used to obtain a value for d_0, including measuring a powdered sample of the material, an annealed sample or a point within a sample that is likely to be free from stress, or using the fact that the residual stresses must balance overall to zero to deduce d_0. For most laboratory-based X-ray measurements, where the measurement is very close to the surface and plane-stress conditions can be assumed, no stress-free reference is needed. Figure 7.33 shows a sample being measured on a laboratory X-ray diffractometer.

Figure 7.34 shows the residual stress profile determined in a welded aluminium plate. The data were obtained using a combination of neutron and high-energy X-ray diffraction. Neutron methods have the advantage of very high penetrability into materials, but access to the dedicated sources that produce neutrons is restricted. Figure 7.35 shows a large component being measured at a neutron diffractometer. High-energy ('synchrotron') X-ray sources are just as difficult to access, but measurements can be obtained extremely quickly. The reason a combination of the two methods was needed in this case is that synchrotron X-rays use very low

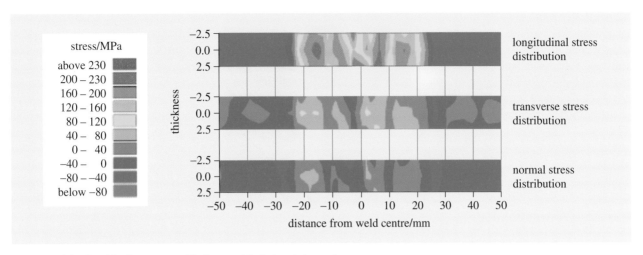

Figure 7.34 Residual stress profile in a welded aluminium plate

Figure 7.35 Large aerospace component being measured at the ENGIN-X diffractometer at the ISIS neutron source, UK

diffraction angles (typically <10°) in comparison to neutron methods. A small diffraction angle (Figure 7.36a) results in a longer path length, for measurements the same depth into the surface, than a large diffraction angle (Figure 7.36b). The strain direction is the bisector of the diffraction angle, so taking strain measurements in two directions using a small diffraction angle can result in a very long path length at one orientation, as shown in Figure 7.36(c). Of course, this will depend on the precise size and shape of the sample, but in practice it means that synchrotron X-rays are unsuitable for measuring the normal strain direction (the component perpendicular to the surface) in many engineering specimens.

Figure 7.36   Path-lengths for (a) small and (b) large diffraction angles; (c) change in path length with direction of strain measurement for the same diffraction angle

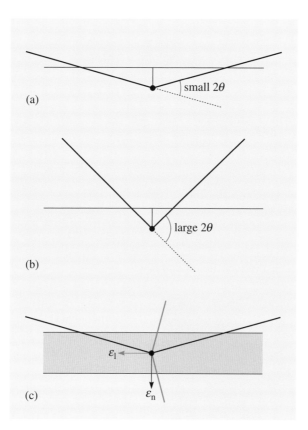

(a) small 2θ

(b) large 2θ

(c) ε_1 ε_n

SAQ 7.5 (Learning outcome 7.4 and revision)

Figure 7.37 shows the measured strains along the centre-line of the welded aluminium plate for which the stress results are shown in Figure 7.34. Assuming that the measured strains shown are in the principal strain directions, calculate the longitudinal residual stress σ_1:

(a)   at the weld centre (0 on the x-axis)

(b)   at +20 mm from the weld centre

(c)   at +40 mm from the weld centre.

The elastic properties of the aluminium are $E = 70$ GPa and $v = 0.34$.

As a reminder, from Block 1 Part 2, the stress is calculated using:

$$\sigma_1 = \frac{E}{(1+v)(1-2v)}\left[(1-v)\,\varepsilon_1 + v\varepsilon_2 + v\varepsilon_3\right]$$

Note that neither plane stress nor plane strain can be assumed.

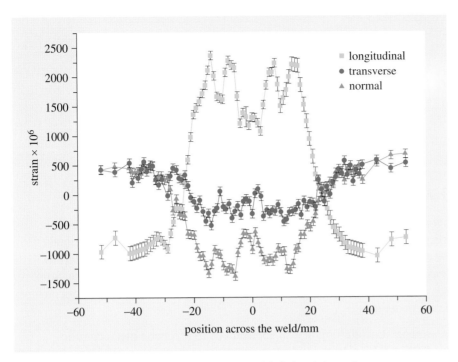

Figure 7.37   Measured residual strains in a welded aluminium plate

4.2.2 Ultrasonic methods

The speed of sound in a material is sensitive to stress. A change in speed can be monitored by measuring the time taken for a pulse of ultrasound to pass through the sample. The velocity of the sound wave depends on the stress as:

$$v = v_0 + k\sigma$$

where v is the measured velocity of the sound wave in the stressed sample, v_0 is the velocity of the sound wave in unstressed material and k is a constant that varies from material to material.

Typical experimental configurations used are shown in Figure 7.38. In each case the ultrasonic waves are launched by transmitting transducers. After propagating through the material, they are detected by a receiving transducer. The technique is called *pulse–echo* when the same transducer is used for sending and detecting the pulse (Figure 7.38a). Another technique, the *pitch–catch* method, involves two different transducers, one for sending the pulse and one for detecting the pulse, as shown in Figure 7.38(b). The stress calculated from these measurements is the *average* stress in the material through which the wave travelled. Therefore, the method does not have a high spatial resolution because the measurements are averaged over large distances. Also, the ultrasound wave velocity may be affected by microstructure, inclusions and inhomogeneities, as well as by the residual stress. Extreme care, therefore, is necessary to interpret the stress result from such ultrasound experiments. The advantages of this method are that measurements can be made relatively quickly, no lengthy experimental set-up procedure is required, there are no radiation hazards and the method is easily portable for *in situ* stress measurements.

Figure 7.38 Ultrasonic stress-measurement techniques: (a) 'pulse–echo'; (b) 'pitch–catch'

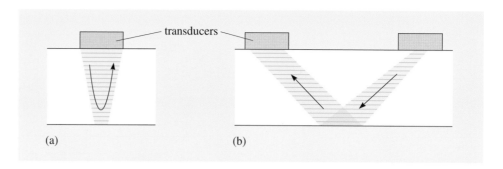

4.2.3 Magnetic methods

There are various stress analysis methods that use the changes in the magnetic properties of materials when a residual stress is present. There are also methods that use changing magnetic fields to induce electric eddy currents into materials, and measurement of the currents can give information about the stress state. Some methods are restricted to magnetic materials; the eddy current methods work on any conductive material.

The measurement depth for practical applications of magnetic methods varies between 0.01 and 3.0 mm, depending upon the frequency range of the signal analysis and the conductivity and 'magnetic permeability' of the test material.

Magnetic stress measurement is a non-destructive, portable and potentially very fast method of stress measurement.

4.2.4 Raman spectroscopy

Another relatively new method for stress measurement is the use of a spectroscopic method called *Raman spectroscopy*. This method is similar to diffraction methods, in that it involves observing the spectral shift in a peak of scattered radiation – usually laser light – from a material, but in this case the peak is produced by scattering of light from the electron clouds around the atoms, rather than by diffraction from the lattice (needless to say, you don't need to know how this works!).

As with diffraction, the shift in the peak of Raman radiation can be correlated to the stress in the material, but in general the response of the Raman peak to stress needs to be calibrated by a control experiment where the peak shift is monitored in response to a known applied stress.

A big advantage of this method is that the material doesn't have to be crystalline for it to work. So it can be applied to polymers and other materials, such as thin films of silicon, which, although crystalline, can be difficult to obtain diffraction patterns from. It's not universally applicable, though, as the material has to show Raman scattering in order for the method to work. In practice, it tends to be applied mostly to polymers, coatings and fibres.

4.3 The range of stress-measurement techniques

This section has intended to give you a flavour of the different types of stress-measurement method that are available. Techniques range from the relatively cheap, such as hole drilling, to the very expensive, such as neutron diffraction, where there

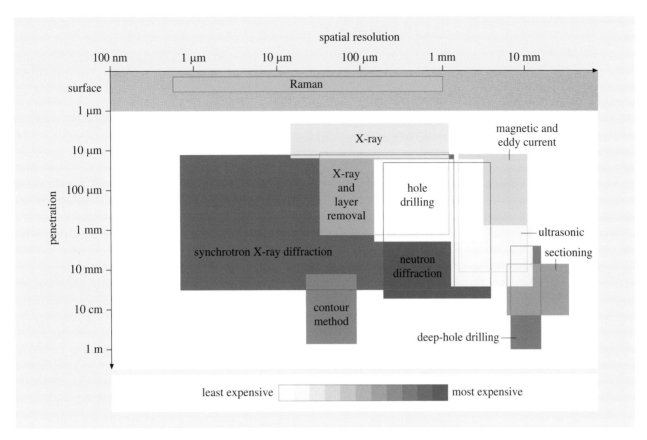

Figure 7.39   Penetration and resolution for a range of stress-measurement techniques

are only perhaps 10–20 facilities worldwide where engineering stress measurements can be performed.

Figure 7.39 summarizes the different methods in terms of their penetration capability (i.e. how deep into a component they can measure), spatial resolution (i.e. how much detail can be obtained) and cost. The cost of a method can be just as important as its capability. The relative costs shown here are indicative only; in practice, the cost of an individual measurement will be a function of the experimental set-up time, the total number of measurements made and the daily operating costs (which can range from tens to thousands of pounds, not including staff time).

SAQ 7.6 (Learning outcome 7.5)

Using the information given in this part, suggest an appropriate method of stress measurement for the following problems.

(a) Determining the near-surface stress (<2 mm) on a scrap crankshaft that has been carburized.

(b) Measuring the full three-dimensional stress tensor non-destructively at a welded joint in a large prototype aircraft component as part of a £10 million development project. The stress field variation needs to be measured with a resolution of 1 mm or better.

(c) Measuring the complete longitudinal stress field in a welded test plate measuring 400 mm × 800 mm × 60 mm.

5 SUMMARY

Broadly speaking, residual stresses can have either a beneficial effect or a deleterious effect, depending on the nature of the component containing the stress, its operating environment and the location and magnitude of the stress.

I have indicated how residual stresses can be introduced deliberately into materials to give a benefit, such as in shot peening, carburizing, tempering of glass and prestressing of concrete.

But they can be deleterious as well. Residual stresses can cause distortion when parts are machined, which can be costly to rectify if tight dimensional tolerances are required. This is particularly problematic during welding, where large stresses can evolve and distort the pieces being joined.

Many of the failure mechanisms you will cover in Block 2, such as fatigue and stress corrosion cracking, can be significantly affected by residual stress if it is a tensile stress in the wrong place. So for now, I want you to be aware that residual stress can be an enemy as well as a friend, and we will return to its effects again later in the course.

To conclude, Figure 7.40 shows an example of where residual stress has led to a component failure. You have already seen how welding causes residual stress. Occasionally, after welds are made, subsequent non-destructive testing might reveal a flaw, from incomplete fusion, or cracking of the weld for some reason (perhaps residual stress!). The original weld would then be ground out and a repair made. Unfortunately, such a repair can elevate the residual stress further and lead to cracking during operation, as shown in Figure 7.40.

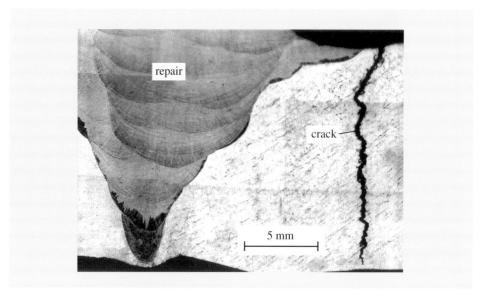

Figure 7.40   Cracking in a power-plant component near to a repaired weld

LEARNING OUTCOMES

After studying Block 1 Part 7 you should be able to do the following.

7.1 Explain the origins of residual stresses in materials, components and assemblies.

7.2 Include the effects of residual stress in calculations of the failure loads of components.

7.3 Give examples of what information is required in the modelling of residual stresses.

7.4 Use data from experimental methods to calculate residual stresses.

7.5 Suggest an appropriate method of stress measurement for a particular problem.

ANSWERS TO EXERCISES

EXERCISE 7.1

In bending, the stress in the beam will vary from compression on one side to tension on the other. The concrete can support the compressive stress by itself, so the steel reinforcement needs to be incorporated only where there are tensile stresses.

EXERCISE 7.2

The stresses vary from peak compression on one side to peak tension at the other. The highest stresses are found at the surfaces of the beam.

EXERCISE 7.3

The overall effect of the process is to make the hole bigger, so its diameter and circumference increase. Thus, at the edge of the hole there is effectively an increase in length, meaning that the hole sees a *tensile* hoop expansion. Material that has been deformed in tension tends to have a compressive residual stress afterwards, so we would expect a compressive stress at the hole edge, which is indeed what happens. Figure 7.41 shows a typical stress profile for a cold-expanded hole.

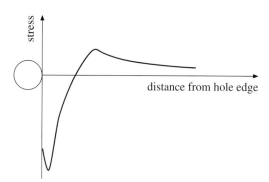

Figure 7.41   Stress profile near a cold-expanded hole

EXERCISE 7.4

The absolute temperature (in kelvin) is related to the temperature in degrees Celsius as:

$$T/\text{K} = \theta/°\text{C} + 273$$

To convert 1400 °C to absolute temperature:

$$T_\text{m}/\text{K} = 1400 + 273 = 1673$$

Therefore $T_\text{m} = 1673$ K. We can then calculate $0.8\,T_\text{m}$:

$$0.8T_\text{m} = 1673 \text{ K} \times 0.8 = 1338 \text{ K}$$

To convert this back to degrees Celsius:

$$\theta/°\text{C} = 1338 - 273 = 1065$$

The stainless steel component would have to be heated to 1065 °C.

EXERCISE 7.5

I came up with the following list, in no particular order (you may have decided on other, equally valid factors):

- the geometry of the steel plate

- the yield stress of the steel as a function of temperature

- the hardening behaviour of the steel

- the elastic properties

- some information about the heat transfer rate from the steel to the oil (which will depend on all sorts of factors – like the oil viscosity, whether it boils to form a gas layer at the steel surface and so on – but which is usually encapsulated in a single parameter)

- the rate of radiative heat loss from the surface.

You may also have thought of the thermal conductivities of the steel and the oil and their specific heat capacities, but these are not usually considered (the specific heat capacity defines how much energy it takes to heat them up: the amount of energy to heat 1 kg of steel by 10 °C will be different from that to heat 1 kg of oil by 10 °C). The quenching medium is assumed to be 'infinite', and the way in which heat is transmitted to it is usually characterized by the last two points above.

ANSWERS TO SELF-ASSESSMENT QUESTIONS

SAQ 7.1

(a) A bolt may carry a residual stress because when it is tightened the force applied to the nut will pull the bolt into tension. There may also be some residual torsion.

(b) In single shear, the shear force carried by the total cross-sectional area has the same magnitude as the external applied tensile force of 12 kN. Hence, each bolt carries a load of 3 kN and experiences a shear stress of:

$$\tau_{xy} = \frac{F}{\pi r^2} = \frac{3 \times 10^3 \text{ N}}{\pi \left(3 \times 10^{-3} \text{ m}\right)^2} = 106 \text{ MPa}$$

(assuming the usual xy-coordinate system with the x-axis horizontal).

To use the Tresca yield criterion we need to know the principal stresses. In a two-dimensional analysis with $\sigma_x = \sigma_y = 0$ and $\tau_{xy} = 106$ MPa, these are the same magnitude as the shear stress. For example, applying the two-dimensional plane-stress equations of Part 1 (or we could use Mohr's circle):

$$\sigma_{\text{max, min}} = \frac{\sigma_x + \sigma_y}{2} \pm \sqrt{\left(\frac{\sigma_x - \sigma_y}{2}\right)^2 + \tau_{xy}^2} = \sqrt{\tau_{xy}^2} = \pm 106 \text{ MPa}$$

But the Tresca criterion is a three-dimensional equation. For plane stress, we simply assume that one of the three principal stresses is zero. So, in three dimensions we have $\sigma_1 = +106$ MPa, $\sigma_2 = 0$ MPa and $\sigma_3 = -106$ MPa. Thus:

$$\sigma_{\text{yield}} = \sigma_1 - \sigma_3 = 106 \text{ MPa} - \left(-106 \text{ MPa}\right) = 212 \text{ MPa}$$

which is just below the yield stress of 220 MPa.

(c) With the extra tensile stress in the bolt we now have $\sigma_y = 50$ MPa and $\tau_{xy} = 106$ MPa. Hence, again assuming $\sigma_2 = 0$, the maximum and minimum principal stresses are:

$$\sigma_{\text{max, min}} = \frac{\sigma_x + \sigma_y}{2} \pm \sqrt{\left(\frac{\sigma_x - \sigma_y}{2}\right)^2 + \tau_{xy}^2}$$

$$= \frac{50}{2} \pm \sqrt{\left(\frac{-50}{2}\right)^2 + 106^2}$$

$$= 25 \pm 109 \text{ MPa}$$

That is, $\sigma_1 = 134$ MPa and $\sigma_3 = -84$ MPa. Applying the Tresca criterion again:

$$\sigma_{\text{yield}} = \sigma_1 - \sigma_3 = 134 \text{ MPa} - \left(-84 \text{ MPa}\right) = 218 \text{ MPa}$$

So the large extra tensile stress still isn't quite enough to cause yield. Phew!

SAQ 7.2

(a) When the welded material cools, its contraction will be constrained by the surrounding material. As it will be unable to contract to a 'stress-free' level, it will be held in residual tension.

(b) The surrounding material will experience a compressive force from the contracting material of the weld, and so will have a compressive residual stress.

SAQ 7.3

(a) If the oxide remains firmly bonded to the metal, then the oxide's expansion will be constrained by the bulk of the parent material. Therefore, the oxide will be placed in compression.

(b) If the oxide is separated from the metal, then the oxide will have no residual stress within it, as it will be free to expand to its stress-free volume.

SAQ 7.4

This could be a long list, but some of the key parameters are:

- the geometry of the weld

- any clamping forces applied to the pieces being welded

- the materials' elastic, plastic and thermal properties, and how they vary with temperature, as well as the melting point of the material(s) being joined

- the heat energy input from the welding heat source, and how fast it moves.

SAQ 7.5

(a) At the weld centre the values are (taking ε_1 to be the longitudinal direction strain, ε_2 to be the transverse direction strain and ε_3 to be the normal direction strain):

$$\varepsilon_1 = 1250\mu\varepsilon$$

$$\varepsilon_2 = -300\mu\varepsilon$$

$$\varepsilon_3 = -800\mu\varepsilon.$$

Therefore:

$$\sigma_1 = \frac{E}{(1+v)(1-2v)}\left[(1-v)\varepsilon_1 + v\varepsilon_2 + v\varepsilon_3\right]$$

$$= \frac{70\times10^9}{(1+0.34)(1-0.68)}\left[(1-0.34)\times1250 + (0.34\times-300) + (0.34\times-800)\right]\times10^{-6}$$

$$= 74 \text{ MPa}$$

(b) At +20 mm from the weld centre the values are:

$$\varepsilon_1 = 950\mu\varepsilon$$

$$\varepsilon_2 = -200\mu\varepsilon$$

$$\varepsilon_3 = -500\mu\varepsilon.$$

Thus:

$$\sigma_1 = \frac{70 \times 10^9}{(1+0.34)(1-0.68)}\left[(1-0.34) \times 950 + (0.34 \times -200) + (0.34 \times -500)\right] \times 10^{-6}$$

$$= 64 \text{ MPa}$$

(c) At +40 mm from the weld centre the values are:

$$\varepsilon_1 = -1000\mu\varepsilon$$

$$\varepsilon_2 = 500\mu\varepsilon$$

$$\varepsilon_3 = 400\mu\varepsilon.$$

Thus:

$$\sigma_1 = \frac{70 \times 10^9}{(1+0.34)(1-0.68)}\left[(1-0.34) \times -1000 + (0.34 \times 500) + (0.34 \times 400)\right] \times 10^{-6}$$

$$= -58 \text{ MPa}$$

SAQ 7.6

(a) As the crankshaft is a scrap part, we don't have to use a non-destructive method. So hole drilling is an option, as is X-ray diffraction, either with or without layer removal. Magnetic methods might work, though they could be confused by the change in composition through the carburized layer.

(b) Neutron diffraction would be needed here: it's the best choice for large components when all stress components are needed with good spatial resolution. Synchrotron X-ray diffraction might be possible depending on the actual geometry; but remember the problem of absorption highlighted in Figure 7.36.

(c) For a large component like this, where the complete distribution of one stress component is required, the contour method would be ideal.

ACKNOWLEDGEMENTS

Grateful acknowledgement is made to the following sources:

FIGURES

Figure 7.1: Gian Lorenzo Bernini © Bettmann/CORBIS.

Figure 7.6: © Science Museum/Science & Society Picture Library.

Figure 7.15: 'Who Determines The Strength of a Part?', Richard Jacobs and Company.

Figure 7.39: Reproduced courtesy of Prof. Philip Withers, University of Manchester.

Figure 7.40: Bouchard, P. (2001) 'Residual Stress in Lifetime and Structural Integrity Assessment', Encyclopedia of Materials Science and Technology, Elsevier Science Ltd.

COURSE TEAM ACKNOWLEDGEMENTS

This part was prepared for the course team by Michael Fitzpatrick and Mark Turski, with contributions by Martin Rist.

T357 COURSE TEAM

Professor Michael Fitzpatrick (course team chair)

Andy Harding (course manager)

Jackie Burnicle (course manager)

ACADEMIC STAFF

Dr Alun Armstrong

Professor Adrian Demaid

Professor Chris Earl

Professor Lyndon Edwards

Dr Salih Gungor

Michael Hush

Dr Peter Lewis

Dr Jim Moffatt

Dr Ed Murphy

Dr Martin Rist

EXTERNAL ASSESSOR

Professor Lindsay Greer, University of Cambridge

CONSULTANTS

David Sefton (critical reader)

Dr Mark Turski

SUPPORT STAFF

Debbie Derbyshire (course team secretary)

Colin Gagg

Stan Hiller

Pete Ledgard

Rehana Malik

PRODUCTION TEAM

Kirsten Barnett

Annette Booz

Philippa Broadbent

Lisa Carrick

Teresa Cox

Sarah Crompton

Daphne Cross

Anna Edgley-Smith

Vicky Eves

Chris French

Carol Houghton

Jonathan Martyn

Katie Meade

Lara Mynors

Deana Plummer

Lynn Short

Susanne Umerski